ARCHITECTURAL DRAWING
FOR THE
BUILDING TRADES

ARCHITECTURAL DRAWING

FOR THE

BUILDING TRADES

BY

JOSEPH E. KENNEY

*Architect; Instructor in Drafting, South Boston High School
Instructor in Blueprint Reading and Estimating
Massachusetts University Extension
Author of "Blueprint Reading for the Building Trades"*

AND

JOHN P. McGRAIL

*Supervisor in Education in Charge of Industrial Classes
Division of University Extension
Massachusetts Department of Education*

FIRST EDITION

McGRAW-HILL BOOK COMPANY, INC.
NEW YORK TORONTO LONDON
1949

76895

ARCHITECTURAL DRAWING FOR THE BUILDING TRADES

This book
is dedicated by the authors
to their wives
as a token of appreciation for their
encouragement and patience
during the period of its writing

Preface

The purpose of this book is to provide practical instruction in drafting. It is designed especially for the following groups:

1. *Students* who wish to prepare themselves for work in an architect's office.
2. *Trainees* and *junior draftsmen* in architectural offices.
3. *Foremen* and *tradesmen* who know how to read blueprints and want to know how to make a drawing.
4. *Builders* and *contractors* who want to know how to prepare simple drawings for everyday jobs.
5. *Estimators* who want to learn the technical phases of modern building practice.

The book can be used as a text in classwork and has many features that will appeal to both student and instructor. However, it is so prepared and written that it can be utilized just as profitably by the person who is unable to attend class and who wishes to train himself.

There are many excellent texts on architectural design. This book does not pretend to cover that field, nor does it concern itself with architecture as a fine art. It is exclusively a manual of instruction in drafting. It is elementary enough for the beginner, but there is plenty of material for the person who has had some training in drawing. Even though the book is intended primarily as a fundamental text on drafting, there are enough construction details and working drawings to make it an excellent handbook for trainees in architects' offices, and for contractors and builders.

The selection and arrangement of material are the result of the authors' combined experience in teaching and supervising classes in practical draftsmanship and twenty years of experience as an architect. The "step-by-step" method is followed, each "step" being taken in the order an architect would draw it. Emphasis throughout the book is placed on practicality rather than theory.

The authors take the student through the detailed drawings before introducing him to small-scale plans and elevations, because they feel that the student should be familiar with the various important parts of a building and the construction of them before he starts to draw plans and elevations. Thus, when he is called upon to indicate a door, or window, or cornice on a $\frac{1}{4}''$ drawing, he will know how it is constructed and will be able to approach the project with greater understanding.

The authors wish to take this opportunity to thank the many architects, contractors, teachers, and others whose advice, criticisms, and suggestions have proved of invaluable assistance in the preparation of this book. Particularly they are indebted to Royal Barry Wills, the noted architect, for his gracious Foreword; to Robert C. Dean, registered architect, for the splendid sketch of the plywood house; to William M. Cameron for his helpful criticism; to the Eagle Pencil Company for permission to use Tips on Techniques; to the Eugene Dietzgen Company for illustrations of drawing instruments; and to Miss Catherine Dunphy for the many long week ends she sacrificed in typing the manuscript.

JOSEPH E. KENNEY
JOHN P. MCGRAIL

BOSTON, MASS.
January, 1949

Contents

CONTENTS

List of Plates

Figure

Foreword

The matter of architectural education has always been a favorite tilting ground for professionals, and in these years of transition the issues seem even sharper; lances are hurled with an almost impolite vigor. Yet there are points of agreement.

Admittedly the teaching of architecture at the college level has never been complete, if only for lack of time. It has striven to impart basic concepts of architectural design, with various collateral subjects to liberalize the student's approach and mechanize his initial attack on the main problem. It carries him to a point where he has a picture of a building, perhaps brilliantly conceived and presented, but only a picture.

Men of all viewpoints regret that the great complex of technical information and precisely prepared drawings that lies between this first stage and the erection of the building has been largely a mystery to the student upon leaving school. He has had to fill the gap through slow personal observation as an apprentice and draftsman in after years.

Now, at last, to find so many of these invaluable data brought together and coordinated here in the book by Joseph E. Kenney and John P. McGrail should be most encouraging to teacher, student, and architect. It gives the why and how of drawing preparation and building construction, and not as a miscellany of useful though unrelated facts, but fashioned as a stout, progressive ladder of practical architectural information on whose rungs the student may greatly speed his climb to active usefulness in an architectural office.

ROYAL BARRY WILLS, A.I.A.

How to Use This Book

Where it is to be used as a basic text in classroom instruction, this book will be supplemented by the teacher's explanations, diagrams, and illustrative material. The student will be referred to standard books on carpentry and masonry construction, on architectural design, and on lettering and other details of drafting for additional instruction and for further practice material. Current magazines on homes and building, architects' journals, building trades' periodicals, handbooks of the various building industries, and manufacturers' catalogues should be studied in order to keep abreast of new developments in the field. Pictures, charts, and models will help the student visualize the work he is doing. Visits to buildings under construction where the student will have the opportunity to see the workman carry out the work indicated by an architect's plans will be of great assistance.

The amount of time to be devoted to each lesson will vary according to the difficulty of the drawing and the aptitude of the student, but, generally speaking, this text will supply ample work for a full course in architectural drafting. Some teachers will wish to assign additional practice material and additional problems, in order to provide for a longer course. The material and arrangement may also be adapted for short-term courses by assigning a considerable portion of the work to be done outside of the class sessions. The instructor in such a course can devote most of the class time to instruction and to criticism of the work done outside.

The student who wishes to use the book for self-instruction will find it complete in every respect. However, he will find it advisable to do as much as possible of the outside reading that is indicated above. In fact, because he will not have an instructor and guide, it is even more important for him to saturate himself in the literature of the field. Such a student will find that he can develop progressively by doing the work indicated in each lesson. He should study the text material carefully, analyze the drawings given in the book, scrutinize the dimensions and directions, refer to the figures indicated, and then go to work, following the step-by-step procedures given.

If difficulties are encountered, he should go back over the textual description, study the drawing again, examine even more minutely the specifications and directions, and then go back step by step over the work done. In almost every case, the student will find that he has made an error which, if corrected, will eliminate his difficulty.

The student should refer continually to the figures and text of the lessons he has completed and should consult the glossary of architectural and building terms on page 123 whenever he encounters an expression that he does not understand.

If it is possible to obtain other plans for study, the student should by all means do so. He should copy as many plans as he can and discuss his problems with architects and contractors. He should draw, and draw some more. When he has finished the book and has satisfactorily completed all the assigned problems, he will not be an architect but he will be a good draftsman, and will be on the threshold of a great and satisfying career—that of architecture. Success in the achievement of that career depends on only one person—the student himself.

LESSON 1

Drawing Instruments and How to Use Them

It is axiomatic in the trades that good workmanship requires good tools and that a good workman takes care of his tools. This is equally true of the good draftsman. There are certain essential tools he will need. These should be of the best quality he can afford and should be treated with the respect they deserve. A lifetime of useful service will reward the observance of this rule.

Drawing Board. This should be no smaller than 18″ x 24″ but preferably should be at least 24″ x 30″. It should have a flat, smooth surface of soft wood and be so constructed that it will not warp or split. The working edge should be tested with a steel straightedge.

T-square. A 30″ T-square, tested for a true edge, will prove adequate for all the work described in this book. The head of the T-square is always held against the *left* working edge of the board (see Fig. 1). The pencil is always drawn along the *upper* edge of the blade and always from left to right. (If the draftsman is left-handed, the T-square will be held against the *right* working edge of the board and lines will be drawn from right to left.)

FIGURE 1

Place the paper in position on the board. Lay the T-square on the upper edge of the paper, holding the head of the T-square against the left edge of the board. With the right hand adjust the paper until its upper edge coincides with the upper edge of the square. Place a thumbtack in the upper left-hand corner, then in the opposite corner, and finally tack the other two corners.

Small (¼″) flat-headed tacks should be used and should be pressed down fast against the paper. Drafting tape may be used instead of thumbtacks.

FIGURE 2

Triangles. One transparent celluloid 8″ 45° triangle and one 10″ 30-60° triangle will be needed to draw vertical lines and angles of the degrees indicated.

To draw vertical lines proceed as follows:

1. Hold the head of the T-square firmly against the left edge of the drawing board.
2. Slide the triangle along the upper edge of the T-square to the desired position on the paper. The triangle should be to the *right* of the line to be drawn.
3. With the left hand hold both the T-square and the triangle in position.
4. Draw *over the edge* of the triangle. Do not draw *up against the edge*. This rule also applies to lines drawn with the T-square (see Fig. 2).

Good professional practice calls for observance of these rules of drawing. Obviously, there will be occasions when it may be necessary or desirable to have the triangle to the *left* of the line to be drawn or to guide your pencil against the edge of the T-square or triangle; but these will be exceptions, and the good draftsman will follow the accepted methods whenever possible.

1

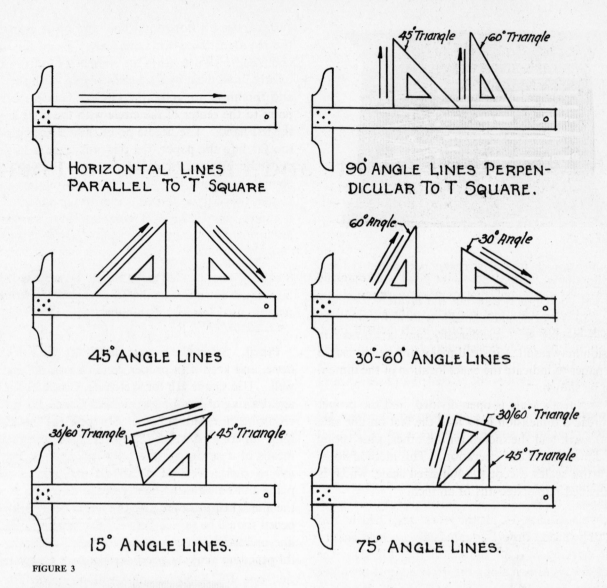

HORIZONTAL LINES PARALLEL TO T SQUARE

90° ANGLE LINES PERPENDICULAR TO T SQUARE.

45° ANGLE LINES

30°-60° ANGLE LINES

15° ANGLE LINES.

75° ANGLE LINES.

FIGURE 3

In addition to 30, 45, 60, and 90° angles, which can be drawn with these triangles, a combination of the T-square and the triangles can indicate 15 and 75° angles as well (see Fig. 3).

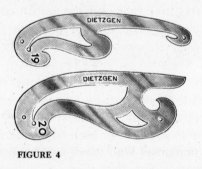

FIGURE 4

Curves. For ruling curved lines other than circle arcs, irregular curves or French curves are used. Various combinations of parts of ellipses, spirals, and mathematical curves are available (see Fig. 4). Care should be taken in drawing curves to maintain smoothness and continuity of the line by adjusting the curve constantly through its successive positions so that it coincides for a little distance with the part already drawn. Breaks, humps, and other irregularities will thus be avoided.

Scale. Any size building or object can be represented on paper by means of scale. The architect selects some smaller dimension to represent a foot and reduces all his dimensions to this unit. For example, he may decide $\frac{1}{8}'' = 1'-0''$; thus, a 40-foot building would occupy only 5 inches on the paper. For convenience, an architect's scale has been devised (see Fig. 5). It is a ruler on which various dimensions are marked off to represent one foot. The student must learn to use the scale and to take off dimensions from the scale indicated on the drawing, as this is fundamental in draftsmanship. Of course, when a draftsman decides on the scale he is going to use in a particular drawing, he must not change that scale in that drawing. In drawing to scale, it is important also to think of and to speak of

FIGURE 5

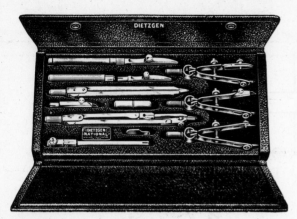

FIGURE 6

each dimension in its full size and not in the reduced size shown on the paper.

It is not good practice to use the dividers to pick a dimension off a scale and transfer it to a drawing; for the dividers may shift accidentally, and a mistake in dimension may result. Instead make tiny pencil marks on the paper to indicate the exact location of the dimension to be shown.

The architect's scale is open-divided, and the proper way to read a dimension is to read the feet on one side of the 0 mark and the inches on the other, thus laying off the dimension in one operation. This method holds good for all scales except the full-sized scale, which is chain-divided into sixteenths of an inch.

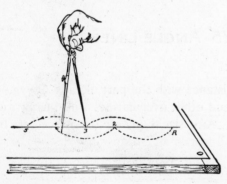

FIGURE 7

Drawing Instruments. The set illustrated in Fig. 6 will suffice for all work shown in this book. The various tools will be described below.

Dividers. It is important to learn how to use the dividers quickly and accurately. The instrument should be held so that the thumb and forefinger will close it and the third and fourth fingers open it. Thus, equal distances can be marked off or a line or space divided into equal parts (see Fig. 7).

Compasses. These are similar to dividers and are used to draw circles and arcs of circles. The lead should be sharpened to a *chisel* point. Never set the compasses for a radius by holding them on a scale.

Instead, draw a horizontal line, and on it measure off the required radius with the scale. From this set the compasses. When using the compasses to draw circles or arcs, hold them by the head, twisting with the thumb and forefinger to make the circle. Guide the needle point to the center of the circle with the little finger of the left hand. The needle point should not be pressed too far into the paper, for this will leave a large hole and may also result in inaccuracy. The legs of the compasses should be "bowed" in drawing large circles so that they will be perpendicular to the paper. Figure 8 shows another type of compass, also known as a *professional bow pencil.*

FIGURE 8

Pencil. Select the proper pencil for the work to be done, and keep it in proper condition to do the work well. Use Grade HB for sketching, Grade H for average drafting or lettering work, and Grade 2H for work requiring fine, sharp lines. Sharpen the pencil to a long, tapering point, and keep the point sharpened by means of a sandpaper pad. Always draw a line from *left* to *right*. The pencil should move in a vertical plane and be inclined slightly in the direction in which the line is being drawn. As the line is being drawn, the pencil should be turned between the fingers to keep the line uniformly sharp and clear. Neat, accurate, careful penciling marks a good draftsman. Cultivate it.

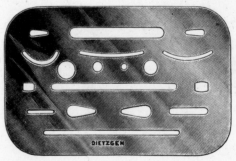

FIGURE 9

Eraser. Too much erasing indicates failure to follow the advice given above. However, even the best of draftsmen will occasionally need to erase; it is often said that a draftsman who never uses an eraser never does any work. For this purpose, a Faber Ruby eraser may be used for either pencil or ink lines on paper or on tracing cloth. Use an erasing shield to protect the paper and the line to be retained (see Fig. 9). For the removal of smudges and light layout lines use artgum, passing it gently from left to right over the drawing (see Figs. 10 and 11 for tips on technique).

Keep your paper clean-spread preparation on working surface before beginning project.

Remove lead dust from pencil point after each sharpening.

Keep your table clean-cover all of the board except the immediate working area.

Keep drafting tools clean wash them often with carbon-tetrachloride and a piece of cotton.

Courtesy of The Eagle Pencil Company.

FIGURE 10

TIPS ON TECHNIQUE

I'M "BENDY"

I've got the creasing business cornered. "Ripper" helps me out on old drawings.

I'M "RIPPER"

My friends are staples, poor scissors and rubber bands. I hate tape.

I'M "SWIPER"

I'm the guy who steals the arrow heads which are'nt there.

I'M "STUMPY"

Boy! Am I dull! Sharp pencils annoy me.

I'M "CRUMBY"

I eat my lunch on your board. Grease spots are my work.

I'M "SKIDDER"

I slide on clean T squares and Triangles and make them dirty.

Courtesy of The Eagle Pencil Company.

FIGURE 11

5

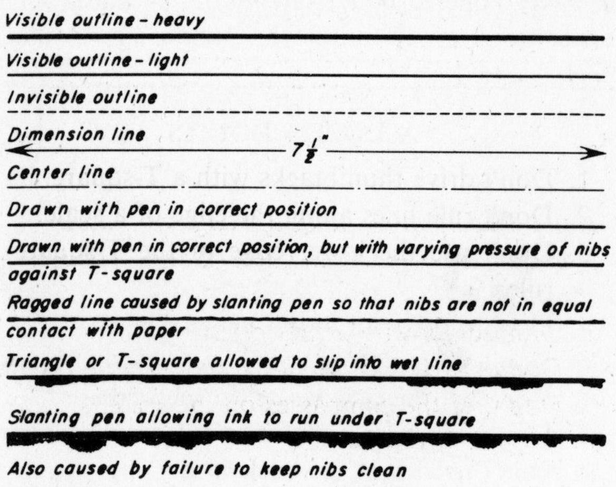

Visible outline - heavy

Visible outline - light

Invisible outline

Dimension line   7½"

Center line

Drawn with pen in correct position

Drawn with pen in correct position, but with varying pressure of nibs against T-square

Ragged line caused by slanting pen so that nibs are not in equal contact with paper

Triangle or T-square allowed to slip into wet line

Slanting pen allowing ink to run under T-square

Also caused by failure to keep nibs clean

FIGURE 12

Drawing Paper. There are various grades and types of drawing paper. The good draftsman will choose a paper suitable for the work he is doing. He will look for one agreeable in appearance with sufficient grain, or "tooth," to take even pencil lines. The paper must be able to take erasures and still show a clean-cut inked line on the erased surface. Experience and the advice of good dealers will be the best guide in the selection of papers and tracing cloths. The saving of a few pennies on bargain materials is not economy.

Ruling Pen. This is used to rule lines in ink. Fill the pen by using the quill on the ink-bottle stopper, taking care not to fill it too much and not to get any ink on the outside of the pen. About $\frac{1}{4}$" of ink is sufficient. The width of the line may be varied by adjusting the screw on the pen. Sharpen the pen on a hard, fine oilstone. The point must be neither too sharp nor too rounded; practice on several old pens with frequent testing for results will be justified by the satisfaction derived from using a well-sharpened pen. Figure 12 shows faulty lines, the result of improper inking.

Inking. Always use the ruling pen with a guiding edge. Use the triangle with the T-square. Adjust the screw to give a variation of lines as shown on the line-indication sheet in Fig. 13. Hold the pen against the straightedge with the screw on the outside, the blades parallel to the straightedge, the pen held in a vertical plane inclined slightly to the right. Draw the line with a whole-arm movement until just before the end of the line is reached. Lift the pen when the line is finished, and take away the straightedge without blotting. Never try to connect a curve to a straight line. Draw circles or arcs first, and connect with straight lines afterward. Keep the pen clean, and always wipe the pen completely dry after using. The secret of good inking is to have a clean pen at all times.

Line Indications. Since lines have a kind of language

all their own, they must be drawn so that they convey their message clearly and accurately. Thus, parts of a drawing will be shown in a fairly heavy line and other parts in light lines, for a blueprint would be confusing and most difficult to read if all the lines were the same grade. On a complicated drawing it is very important that the main outline of the plan stands out clearly. The language of lines used on plans may be found on the line-indication sheet (Fig. 13). This shows the standard lines, their proportionate weight, or thickness, and their construction. It also shows how they are used. The various lines are illustrated and numbered for identification by corresponding numbers in the circles shown on the small plan. The various weights of lines, emphasizing the important wall outlines, etc., make it easier to read a drawing, just as a newspaper emphasizes its headlines and important news items.

Lines are defined as follows:

Trim line: A light continuous line along which the tracing is trimmed in order to square up the sheet.

Border line: A heavy continuous line that outlines, or borders, the drawing. The border line expresses the fact that the drawing is complete within this outline.

Main object line: A heavy unbroken line used to show visible outlines or edges that would be seen by a person looking at the article, house, or building.

Dimension line: A dimension line is one drawn to show the distance between two points. The line is a light one, so that it is clear and easy to read at a glance, and has an arrowhead at each end. The arrowhead touches extension lines and center lines drawn from points or edges of the building and indicates the termination of the figure. The dimension in the break or on top of the dimension line gives the exact distance between these points.

Extension line: Extension lines are used together with dimension lines. An extension line is the light line extending from the edge or end of a part and is the line that the arrowhead touches. By following along this light extension line, one sees the point to which the dimension and arrowheads refer.

Equipment line: A light, continuous, unbroken line used to show equipment such as windows, doors, plumbing fixtures, or radiators.

Symbol section line: Symbol section lines are light lines evenly spaced. They are used to shade surfaces shown on a drawing and by this means indicate the material used.

Broken line: A broken line has a wavy break in it at intervals and is used to indicate that parts have been left out or that the full length of some part has not been drawn. Broken lines are most commonly used on detailed drawings, especially full-size details.

Invisible line: This line is one made up of a series of short dashes and is used to indicate hidden or invisible edges—edges that are hidden under some other part of the structure.

Center line: A center line is made up of alternating long and short dashes and is used to locate centers.

Section line: A section line is a solid line with an arrowhead at each end pointing in the direction in which the section is to be taken. The line tells just where the section has been cut through the wall or building. The sections are identified in most cases by the letters *A-A*, *B-B*, etc., although numbers are sometimes used.

Stair indicator: A stair indicator is a solid line with an arrowhead indicating the direction of the run of the stairs. If given as Up 12-R, it means that there are 12 risers from floor to floor and that the stairs go up.

In architectural drawing, it is good practice to cross all corners slightly. This is done to "snap up" a drawing and to give it more character. The beginner should do this very carefully and should not use the practice as an excuse for careless drawing. Crossing the lines too much spoils the effect.

Before leaving the subject of drawing instruments, the student is urged to work faithfully and conscientiously on the problems and exercises assigned at the end of this lesson. The problems in this book have been selected to give the student the practice without which he can never hope to be a draftsman. In addition, he is warned to keep in mind the following "don'ts" as things *not* to do.

A DOZEN DON'TS

1. Don't drive thumbtacks with a T-square.
2. Don't rule lines along the edge of a scale.
3. Don't use the lower edge of the T-square as a ruler.
4. Don't draw with a dull pencil.
5. Don't sharpen a pencil over a drawing board.
6. Don't set the compasses on the scale.
7. Don't jab the dividers into the drawing board.
8. Don't redraw a line backward.
9. Don't use the same thumbtack holes twice.
10. Don't start work until you wipe off table and instruments.
11. Don't forget to clean all instruments after using.
12. Don't forget to loosen the spring on bow instruments.

EXERCISES AND PROBLEMS

1. Line indications. Copy Fig. 13 exactly as shown, making sure to indicate the proper weight of line. Use a 9″ x 12″ sheet.

2. Scale. Copy Fig. 14 using the dimensions and scale given. Use a 9″ x 12″ sheet for each drawing.

LINE INDICATIONS

1. TRIM LINE
2. BORDER LINE
3. MAIN OBJECT LINE
4. DIMENSION LINE
5. EXTENSION LINE
6. EQUIPMENT LINE
7. SYMBOL SECTION LINE
8. BROKEN LINE
9. INVISIBLE LINE
10. CENTER LINE
11. SECTION LINE
12. STAIR INDICATOR

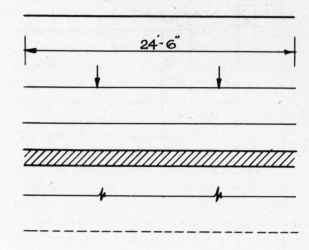

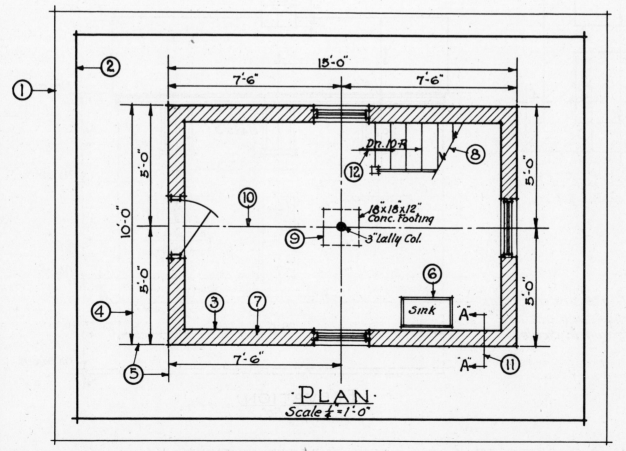

·PLAN·
Scale ¼"=1'-0"

Plan showing how lines are used.

FIGURE 13

8

SCALE PROBLEMS

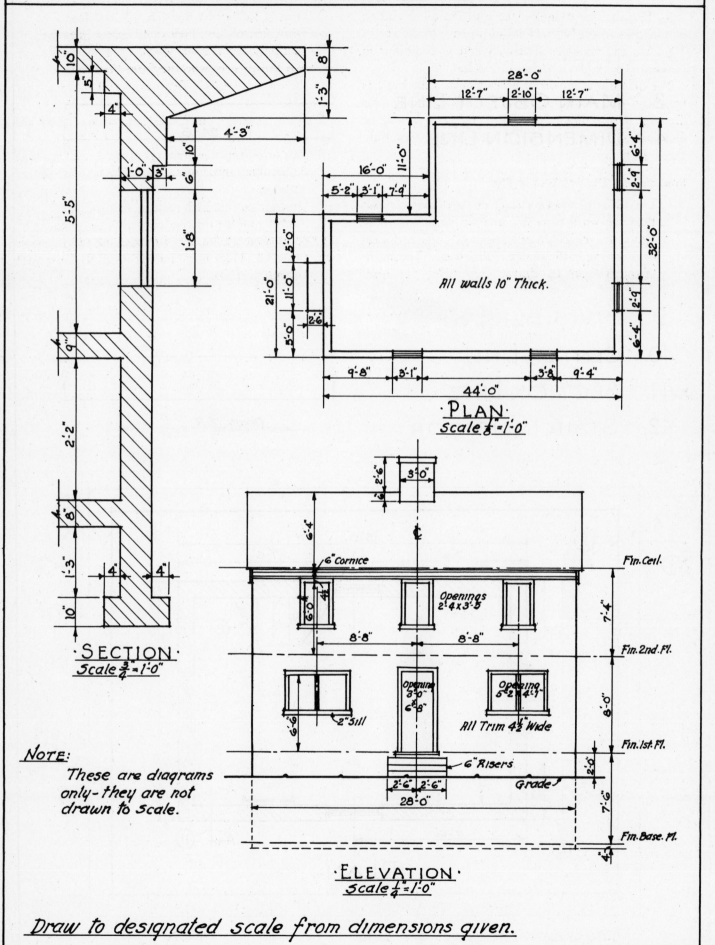

All walls 10" Thick.

·PLAN·
Scale ⅛"=1'-0"

·SECTION·
Scale ¾"=1'-0"

NOTE:

These are diagrams only- they are not drawn to Scale.

6" Cornice

Openings 2'-4 x 3'-5

Opening 3'-0" 6'-8"

Opening 5'-2"x4'-1"

2" Sill

All Trim 4½ Wide

6" Risers

Grade

Fin. Ceil.

Fin. 2nd. Fl.

Fin. 1st. Fl.

Fin. Base. Fl.

·ELEVATION·
Scale ¼"=1'-0"

Draw to designated scale from dimensions given.

FIGURE 14

9

3. T-square and triangles (see Fig. 15). The garden plan shown in Fig. 15 will afford practice in the use of T-square and triangles separately and in combination (see Fig. 3).

The diagram is drawn to no particular scale but has been laid out carefully; and if the student makes his drawing to the dimensions given, the pattern will be identical with that shown. If there is any variation, check all figures and angles.

Procedure for Drawing Garden Plot

1. Use 12″ x 18″ sheet vertically on the drawing board.
2. Plan the work carefully, adding the intermediate figures to get length and width in order to locate the drawing in the center of the sheet. The entire layout should be drawn very lightly at first.

Draw a ½″ border line and title box (see Fig. 17).
3. Draw vertical and horizontal center lines first.
4. Using the dimensions given, draw the entire outline at full size, working from the center lines to the outside edges. Draw center block first; then add wings.
5. With T-square and triangles, draw lightly the diagonal lines as shown.
6. Put in dimension lines as shown, and add all dimensions and notes. (Use guide lines for all lettering.)
7. Go over outline with a clean, heavy line.
8. Study again the instruction on inking (page 6).
9. After some preliminary practice, ink this drawing. Erase all guide lines, and clean up drawing with an artgum eraser.

USE OF T-SQUARE AND TRIANGLES

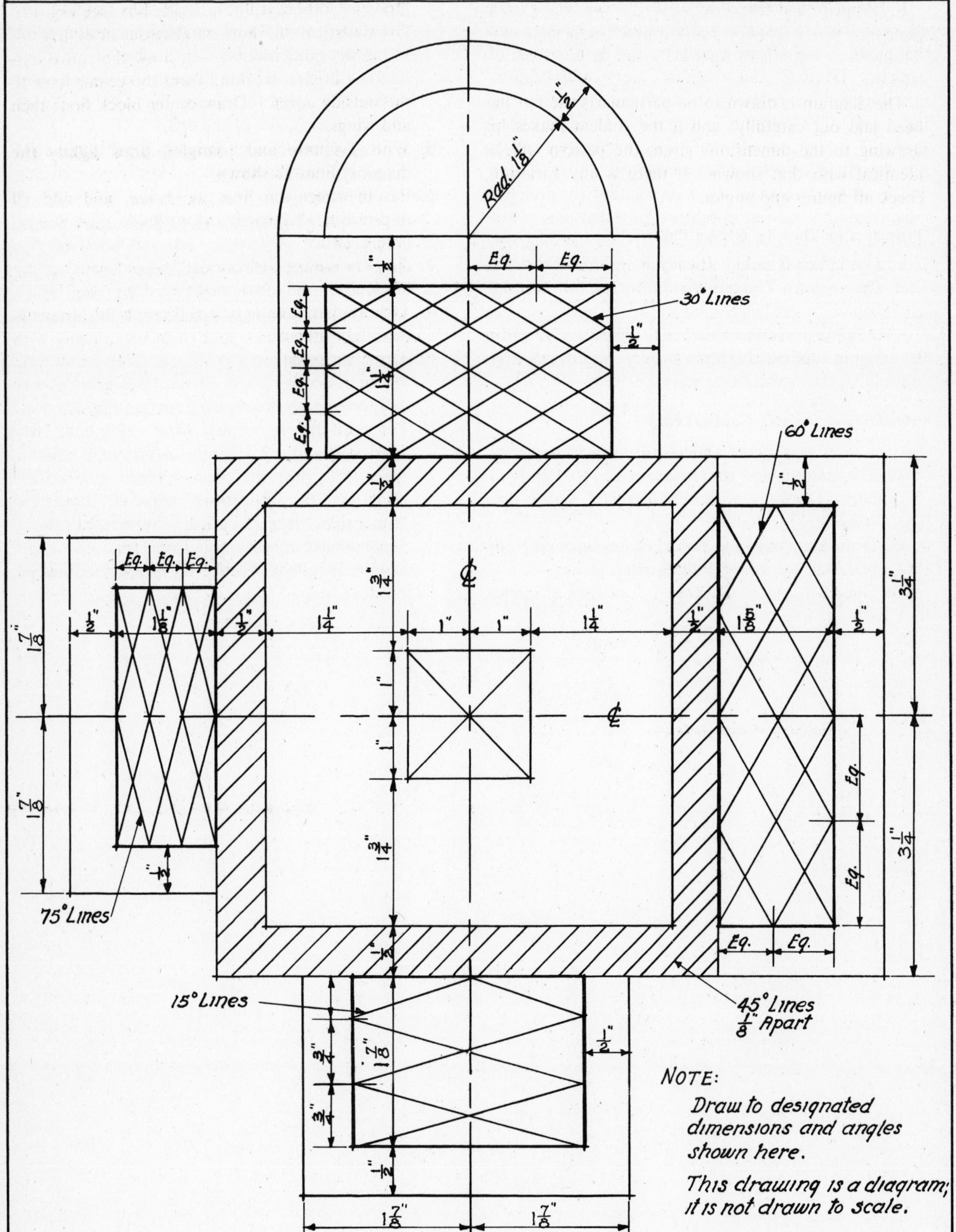

Rad. 1⅛"
½"

Eq. | Eq.

30° Lines

½"

Eq. Eq. Eq. Eq. Eq.

1¼"

½"

60° Lines

½"

Eq. Eq. Eq.

3¾"

3¼"

½"

1⅛"

½"

1¼"

1"

1"

1¼"

1"

1⅝"

½"

¢

¢

1⅞"

½"

3¼"

½"

1⅞"

1¾"

Eq.

Eq.

75° Lines

½"

Eq. Eq.

15° Lines

45° Lines
⅛" Apart

¾"

7⅛"

½"

¾"

NOTE:

Draw to designated
dimensions and angles
shown here.

This drawing is a diagram;
it is not drawn to scale.

1⅞"

1⅞"

FIGURE 15

11

4. Use of instruments. Since the garden latticework shown in Fig. 16 includes arches as well as squares and diagonals, it will afford excellent practice in the use of compass, T-square, and triangles. Very careful draftsmanship will be required to draw the latticework as indicated. The diagram is not drawn to scale; therefore, the student should not measure the lines shown but should follow the figures and notes.

The 60°-angle latticework at each side of the arch has been tried and laid out at full size, and that part of the finished drawing should look exactly like the diagram. If any variation is noted when finished, check dimensions and angles. The center lattice is laid out in equal squares.

Note the use of the center line. Frequently, when the detail is duplicated exactly, the architect draws only one-half of the elevation, as shown here.

Procedure for Drawing Garden Lattice

1. Use 12″ x 18″ sheet, and have drawing well spaced.
2. The entire layout should be drawn very lightly at first. Draw a ½″ border line and a title box (see Fig. 17).
3. Draw base line, and extend center lines up from base-line according to dimensions given.
4. Since it is better practice to draw arcs of circles first and then to connect them with straight lines, the student should now establish the center point of the arcs that will form the arches.
5. Draw a horizontal line through this center point sufficiently long to receive the arcs of circles drawn at each side of the arch.
6. Draw vertical lines of arches tangent to the arcs.
7. Draw top and bottom rails of lattice on each side of the arches.
8. Fill in the 60°-angle latticework.
9. Show lattice in arches. Lay out equal spaces, and draw center lines radiating from center point of arch. With two triangles, draw ¹⁄₁₆″ lattice equally spaced each side of these center lines and parallel to them.
10. Draw lattice squares as shown, using method of laying out equal spaces between two given points as shown in geometric diagram (see Fig. 28).
11. Put in all dimensions and notes, using light lines for dimensions. Use guide lines for all notes and titles. Go over the main outlines with a firm clear line; the latticework, however, should be lighter than the main outline. When the drawing is completed in acceptable form, the student can acquire excellent practice by inking the finished product.

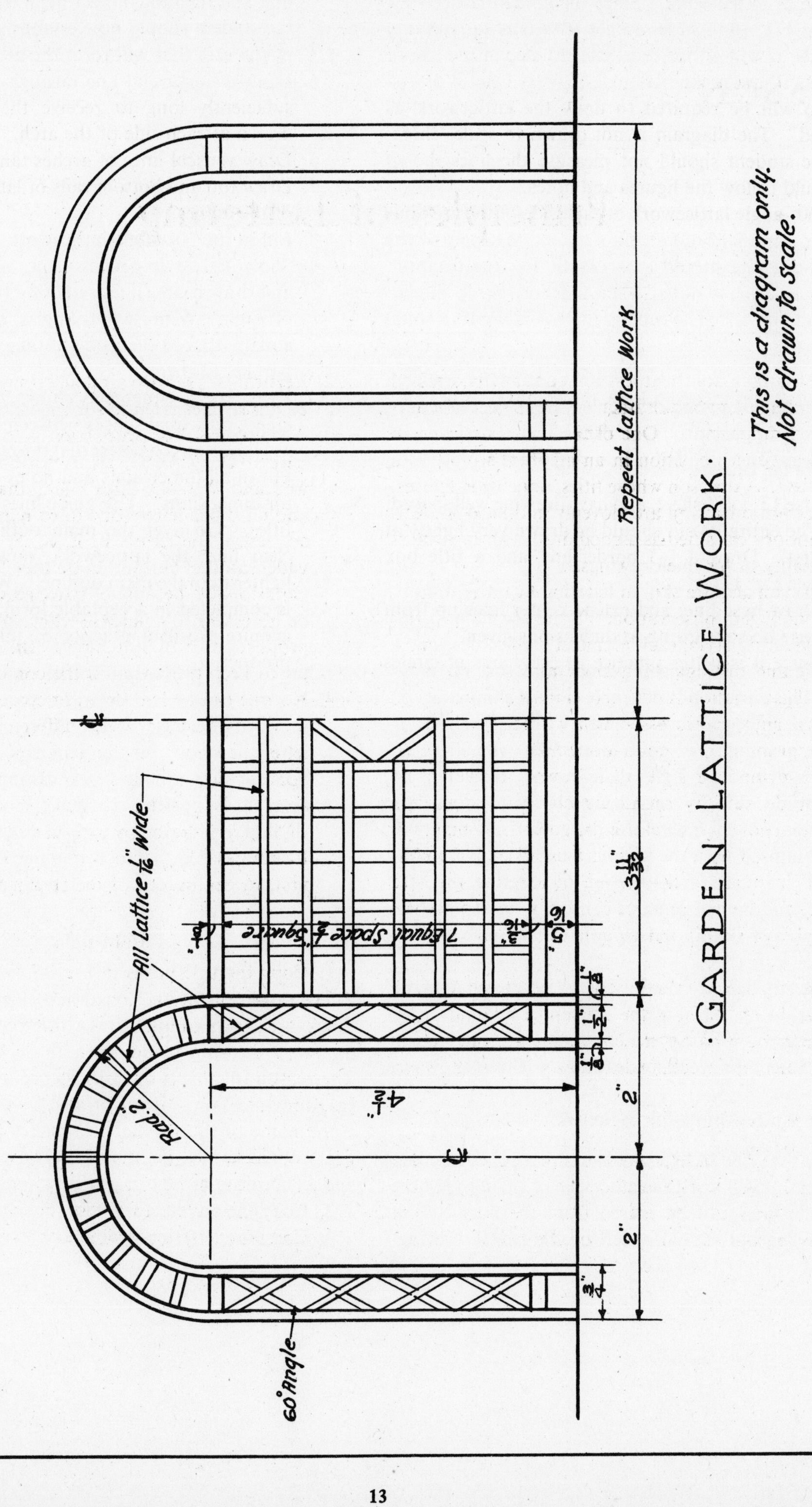

This is a diagram only.
Not drawn to scale.

Repeat Lattice Work

All Lattice $\frac{7}{16}$" Wide

7 Equal Space $\frac{5}{8}$" Square

$\frac{5}{16}$"

$3\frac{11}{32}$"

$\frac{5}{8}$" $\frac{5}{8}$"

$\frac{1}{8}$" $\frac{1}{2}$" $\frac{5}{8}$"

$4\frac{3}{8}$"

2"

Rad. $2\frac{3}{8}$"

2"

$\frac{3}{4}$"

60° Angle

GARDEN LATTICE WORK.

FIGURE 16

13

LESSON 2

Principles of Lettering

Since accuracy and neatness are continually stressed in the training of a good draftsman, the subject of lettering is most important. One of the first tests given to an applicant for a position in an architect's office is a lettering test. A person whose titles, dimension figures, and notes on a drawing are slovenly and hard to decipher cannot be classified as a good draftsman regardless of the quality of his line drawings.

Anyone can acquire skill in lettering by diligent practice and intelligent observation. There are many variations in lettering style, each architect's office desiring a distinctive and distinguishing mode as a sort of trademark. This variation is desirable since it eliminates the mechanical appearance associated with typewriting or lead-type printing. A good draftsman will strive to achieve a distinctive style all his own. However, he must not do this by sacrificing clarity, neatness, or good proportions. Therefore, the good draftsman will acquaint himself with the various pens, books of alphabets, and manuals of instruction in lettering that are available, and he will practice constantly to acquire the same degree of skill in lettering that he has achieved in drawing.

For the novice, it is sufficient to point out that he should begin by learning the single-line adaptation of roman lettering, which is the commonly accepted lettering in architectural working drawings. This is shown in Fig. 18.

Here are a few hints for beginners:

1. The first rule in lettering is to draw penciled guide lines for all work, whether pencil or ink. These guide lines can be erased from the finished ink drawing but should be left on the pencil drawing.

2. Vertical strokes are all made downward and horizontal strokes from left to right.

3. A simple rule for proportion is to make all round letters (O, Q, G, C, D) as wide as they are tall, M's and W's one-third wider than they are tall, and all other letters one-third narrower than they are tall. The letters B, E, K, S, X, Z should be wider at the bottom than they are at the top. Occasionally, because of space requirements, it will be necessary to condense letters so that the above proportions will not apply. In such instances, try to keep proportion in the condensed letters.

4. No rule can be laid down for spacing of letters or of words because of the different widths of the letters, because of the sequence of letters, and because of word and line arrangements. However, it is possible to achieve smoothness and rhythm in lettering by careful attention to spacing. It is advisable to block out the lettering roughly first, to get an idea of the spacing required.

PROBLEMS

1. Copy the title boxes in Fig. 17.

The arrangement and location of a title box, or title block, are shown in Fig. 17. A title box should appear on every drawing made, even those done in school. The reason for this is obvious—since it is conducive to easy identification. It might also be pointed out that, if the name of the person who makes the drawing appears on it, he will be anxious to have it as attractive and as accurate as he can possibly make it.

2. Copy the architectural lettering sheet in Fig. 18.
3. Copy the lettering problem shown in Fig. 19.

TITLE BOXES & SHEET SIZES

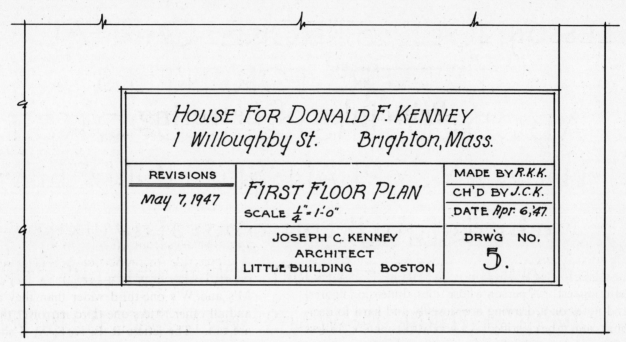

House For Donald F. Kenney
1 Willoughby St. Brighton, Mass.

REVISIONS	FIRST FLOOR PLAN	MADE BY *R.K.K.*
May 7, 1947	SCALE $\frac{1}{4}"=1'-0"$	CH'D BY *J.C.K.*
		DATE *Apr. 6, '47*
	JOSEPH C. KENNEY ARCHITECT LITTLE BUILDING BOSTON	DRW'G NO. 5.

·Typical Title Box Used By Architects' Offices·

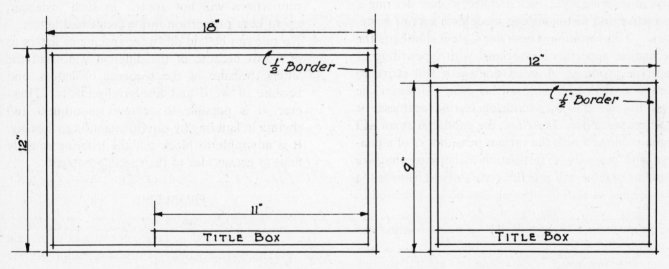

18"

$\frac{1}{2}"$ Border

12"

11"

TITLE BOX

12"

$\frac{1}{2}"$ Border

9"

TITLE BOX

·A Good Standard-Size Sheet For School Work·

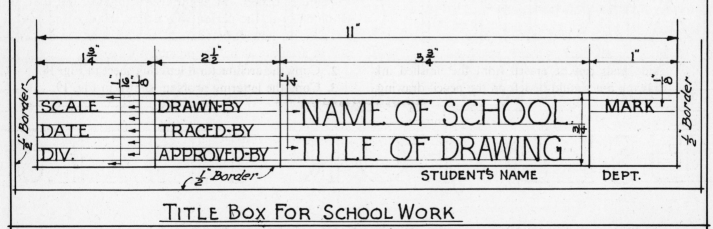

11"

$1\frac{3}{4}"$ $2\frac{1}{2}"$ $3\frac{3}{4}"$ 1"

$\frac{1}{2}"$ Border

SCALE	DRAWN-BY	NAME OF SCHOOL.	MARK
DATE	TRACED-BY	TITLE OF DRAWING	
DIV.	APPROVED-BY		

$\frac{1}{2}"$ Border

STUDENT'S NAME   DEPT.

$\frac{1}{2}"$ Border

Title Box For School Work

FIGURE 17

15

ARCHITECTURAL LETTERING

SINGLE STROKE CAPITAL
LETTERS FOR TITLES
ABCDEFGHIJKLMNOPQRST
UVWXYZ · PLAN · SECTION · ELEV ·

abcdefghijklmnopqrstuvwxyz
VERTICAL SINGLE STROKE ROMAN LETTERS FOR
ARCHITECTURAL DRAWINGS WHEN SPACE IS LIMITED
1234567890 &

ABCDEFGHIJKLMNOPQRSTUVWXYZ 1234567890

$10'\text{-}4''$ $15'\text{-}0\frac{1}{2}''$ $3'\text{-}0''$ $45°\ 30'\ 27''$ $\frac{3}{4}\ \frac{7}{8}\ \frac{1}{2}\ \frac{9}{16}$

ABCDEFGHIJKLMNOPQRSTUVWXYZ

A SLOPING VARIATION OF ABOVE 1234567890

abcdefghijklmnopqrstuvwxyz 60° angle slope
abcdefghijklmnopqrstuvwxyz   This type used mostly for notes.

ABCDEFGHIJKLMN
OPQRSTUVWXYZ
USED FOR TITLES

FIGURE 18

16

LETTERING PROBLEM

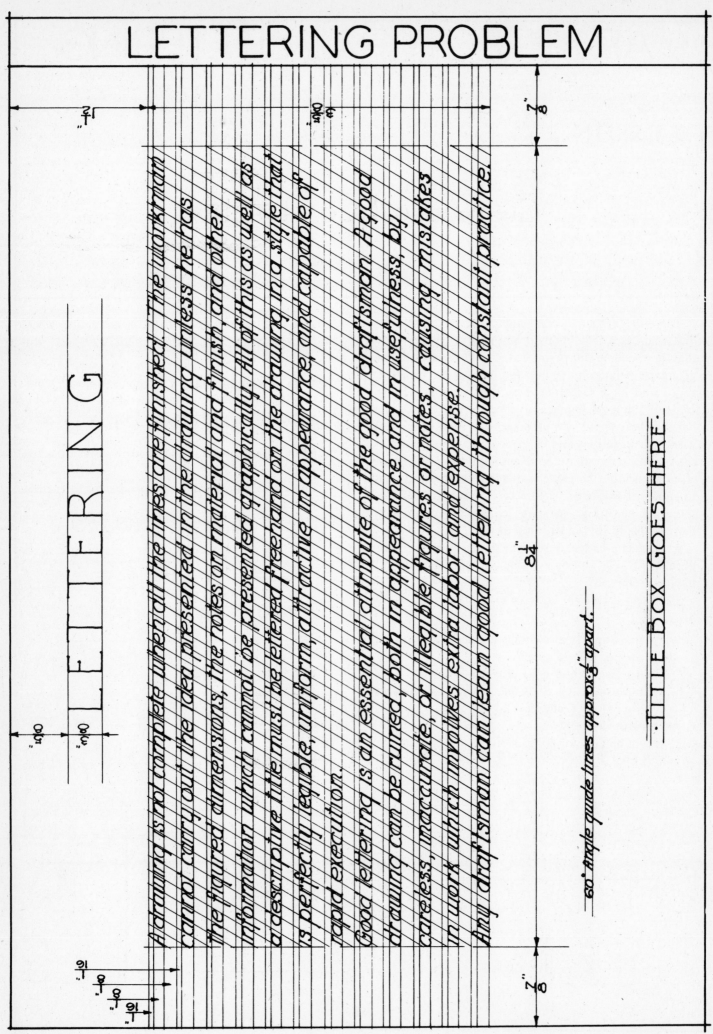

LETTERING

A drawing is not complete when all the lines are finished. The workman cannot carry out the idea presented in the drawing unless he has the figured dimensions, the notes on material and finish, and other information which cannot be presented graphically. All of this as well as a descriptive title must be lettered freehand on the drawing in a style that is perfectly legible, uniform, attractive in appearance and capable of rapid execution.

Good lettering is an essential attribute of the good craftsman. A good drawing can be ruined, both in appearance and in usefulness, by careless, inaccurate, or illegible figures or notes, causing mistakes in work which involves extra labor and expense.

Any draftsman can learn good lettering through constant practice.

60° Angle guide lines approx. ⅛" apart.

·TITLE BOX GOES HERE·

FIGURE 19

17

LESSON 3

Geometrical Construction

There are certain fundamental processes that every draftsman is called upon to accomplish so frequently that they become almost automatic. The study of plane geometry includes many of these, but for the benefit of those who have forgotten these construction exercises some of the most important processes will be outlined here. These should be practiced over and over again with such variations and changes as may suggest themselves until they can be done automatically. Constant reference should be made to plane-geometry texts and to standard works on architectural drawing to expand the draftsman's knowledge of geometric figures and to increase his facility in drawing them.

An excellent review of some of the principles of plane geometry can be had by working out a proof of the following exercises.

To bisect a straight line (see Fig. 20) proceed as follows:

1. Set the compass at a radius greater than one-half of the line to be divided.
2. With A as a center draw a light arc $\widehat{MN}$.
3. With B as a center draw another arc $\widehat{XY}$ intersecting arc $\widehat{MN}$ at C and D.
4. Draw the line CD.
5. O will be the mid-point of AB.

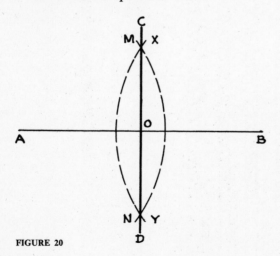

FIGURE 20

To erect a perpendicular from a given line where point O is near the center of the line (see Fig. 21) proceed as follows:

1. With any radius and O as a center, draw arcs cutting the line at A and B.
2. With a radius greater than AO and A as a center, draw arc $\widehat{P}$.
3. With the same radius and B as a center, draw arc $\widehat{R}$ intersecting arc $\widehat{P}$ at C.
4. Draw CO, which will be perpendicular to the line AB at O.

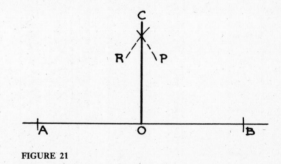

FIGURE 21

To draw a perpendicular to a given line where point O is near the end of the line (see Fig. 22) proceed as follows:

1. With any convenient radius and O as a center, draw the arc $\widehat{AB}$.

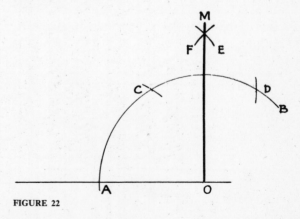

FIGURE 22

2. With the same radius, step off this distance from A to C and from C to D on the arc $\widehat{AB}$.

3. With any radius more than half the distance from C to D and C as a center, draw arc $\widehat{E}$.

4. With the same radius and D as a center, draw arc $\widehat{F}$ intersecting arc $\widehat{E}$ at M.

5. Draw MO, which will be perpendicular to AO.

To draw a perpendicular to a given line where point O is at the end of the line (see Fig. 23) proceed as follows:

1. With any convenient radius and O as a center, draw arc $\widehat{BC}$.

2. With the same radius and B as a center, draw arc $\widehat{E}$ intersecting arc $\widehat{BC}$ at D.

3. Through D draw BD, extending it indefinitely.

4. Still with the same radius and with D as a center, draw arc $\widehat{F}$ intersecting BD at G.

5. Draw GO, which will be perpendicular to BO.

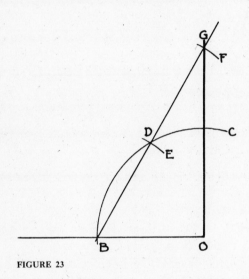

FIGURE 23

To draw a line parallel to a given line at a given distance from that line (see Fig. 24) proceed as follows:

1. With the given distance as radius and with centers at any two points A and B on the line, draw arcs $\widehat{E}$ and $\widehat{F}$.

2. Erect perpendiculars at A and B intersecting the arcs at C and D.

3. Draw line CD tangent to arcs $\widehat{E}$ and $\widehat{F}$, which is the required parallel.

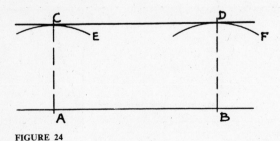

FIGURE 24

To bisect an odd-sized angle (see Fig. 25) proceed as follows:

1. With any convenient radius and O as a center, draw arcs $\widehat{M}$ and $\widehat{N}$ intersecting sides of the angle.

2. With radius slightly larger than the distance from M to N and center at M, draw arc $\widehat{A}$.

3. With the same radius and center at N, draw arc $\widehat{B}$ intersecting arc $\widehat{A}$ at E.

4. Draw EO, which will bisect the angle.

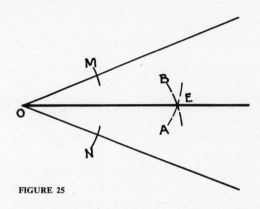

FIGURE 25

To duplicate a given angle (see Fig. 26) proceed as follows:

1. With any convenient radius and apex O of the given angle as center, draw an arc intersecting the sides of the given angle at C and D.

2. With the same radius and X as a center, draw an arc $\widehat{A}$, which will intersect the side of the new angle at M.

3. Set the compass at a radius equal to the distance between C and D. Then, with M as a center, draw arc $\widehat{B}$, which will intersect arc $\widehat{A}$ at N.

4. Draw NX, which will complete the angle NXM equal to angle COD.

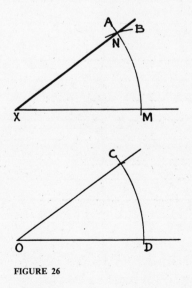

FIGURE 26

To divide a line into any number of equal parts (say 6) (see Fig. 27) proceed as follows:

1. Draw *BD* perpendicular to the given line.
2. Lay the scale so that 0 falls on *A*.
3. Take any multiple (say 12) of the number of equal parts desired, and locate that figure on line *DB*.
4. Draw the line *AD*.
5. Locate on *AD* the required number of divisions.
6. Through each of these points draw a perpendicular to *AB*. This will divide *AB* into the required number of equal parts.

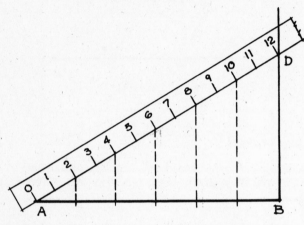

FIGURE 27

To divide a space between two lines into any number of equal parts (say 7) (see Fig. 28) proceed as follows:

1. Lay the scale so that 0 falls on *AB* at *E*.
2. Take any number divisible by 7 (say 21), and locate that number on *CD* at *F*.
3. Draw the line *EF*.
4. Locate on *EF* the required number of divisions.
5. Through each point draw a line parallel to *AB*, which will divide the space into equal parts.

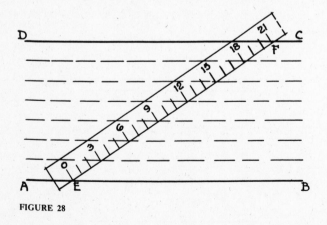

FIGURE 28

To draw a circular intersection between two straight lines (see Fig. 29) proceed as follows:

1. First determine the radius of the circular intersection desired.
2. Draw *EF* parallel to *AB* and at a distance from *AB* equal to the radius selected.
3. Similarly draw *GH* parallel to *CD*.
4. With the same radius and with the intersection *O* as the center, draw an arc connecting lines *AB* and *CD*.

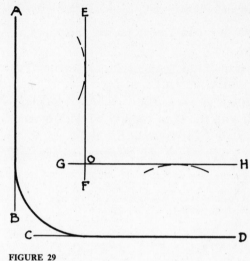

FIGURE 29

To inscribe a pentagon in a given circle (see Fig. 30) proceed as follows:

1. Draw diameters *AB* and *CD* perpendicular to each other.
2. Bisect *OB*.
3. With the point of bisection *E* as a center and *EC* as a radius, draw arc $\widehat{CF}$.
4. With center *C* and radius *CF*, draw arc $\widehat{CG}$.
5. With center *G* and the same radius, draw arc $\widehat{GH}$.
6. Similarly, with the same radius, locate points *I* and *J*. Connect these points.

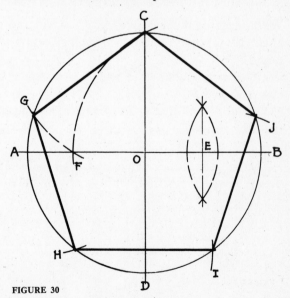

FIGURE 30

To draw a hexagon from a given side (see Fig. 31) proceed as follows:

1. Using the given side as a radius, draw a circle.
2. Draw the diameter *AB*.
3. Still using the given side as a radius and with *B* as a center, draw arcs $\widehat{C}$ and $\widehat{D}$.
4. With the same radius and *A* as a center, draw arcs $\widehat{E}$ and $\widehat{F}$.
5. Connect these points to make the required hexagon.

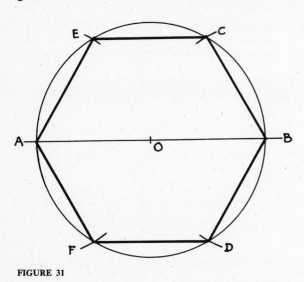

FIGURE 31

To inscribe an octagon in a given circle (see Fig. 32) proceed as follows:

1. Through the center of the circle *E*, draw *AB* and *CD* perpendicular to each other, intersecting the circumference of the circle at *A*, *B*, *C*, and *D*.
2. Bisect the angles *AEC* and *BEC*, and extend the bisectors to intersect the circumference of the circle at *F*, *I*, *G*, and *H*.
3. Connect points *A*, *H*, *D*, *I*, *B*, *G*, *C*, *F*, and *A*, making the required hexagon.

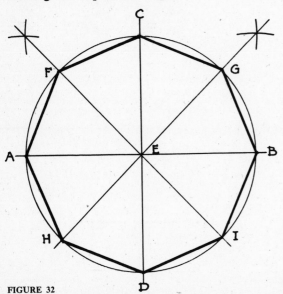

FIGURE 32

To construct a regular octagon within a given square (see Fig. 33) proceed as follows:

1. Draw the diagonals *AC* and *BD*.
2. With *A* as a center and with half the diagonal of the square as a radius, draw arc $\widehat{EF}$.
3. With the same radius and with *B* as the center, draw arc $\widehat{GH}$; with *C* as the center, draw arc $\widehat{LK}$; with *D* as the center, draw arc $\widehat{MN}$.
4. Join points *E* and *K*, *N* and *H*, *L* and *F*, *G* and *M* to make the required octagon.

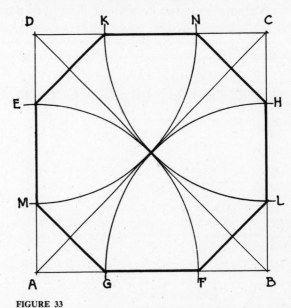

FIGURE 33

To draw a true ellipse using the "trammel" method (see Fig. 34), the major and minor axes being given, proceed as follows:

1. On a straightedge to be used as a trammel, mark off *XY* equal to one-half the minor axis *CD* and *XZ* equal to one-half the major axis *AB*.
2. Move the trammel in successive positions, always keeping *Y* on *AB* and *Z* on *CD*.
3. Mark the locations of point *X* by dots; and when a sufficient number are located, connect them with a French curve.

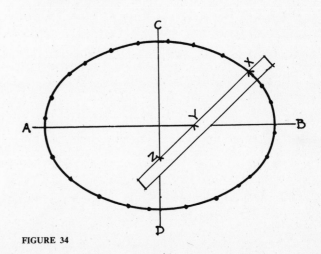

FIGURE 34

To draw an approximate ellipse, the major and minor axes being given (see Fig. 35), proceed as follows:

1. On the minor axis *CD*, lay off *XE* and *XF* equal to the difference between the major and minor axes.
2. On the major axis *AB*, lay off *XG* and *XH* equal to three-quarters of *XE*.
3. Connect points *F* and *H*, *F* and *G*, *E* and *H*, *E* and *G*, extending the lines through *G* and *H*.
4. With center *G* and radius *GA*, draw arc $\overset{\frown}{MAO}$.
5. With center *F* and radius *FC*, draw arc $\overset{\frown}{OCP}$.
6. With center *H* and radius *HB*, draw arc $\overset{\frown}{PBN}$.
7. With center *E* and radius *ED*, draw arc $\overset{\frown}{NDM}$, completing the required ellipse.

GEOMETRIC-DIAGRAM TEST

Perform all the operations indicated in Fig. 36.

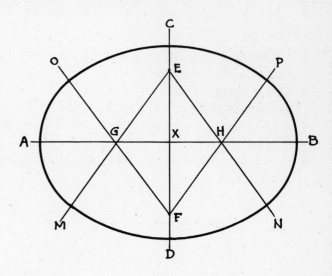

FIGURE 35

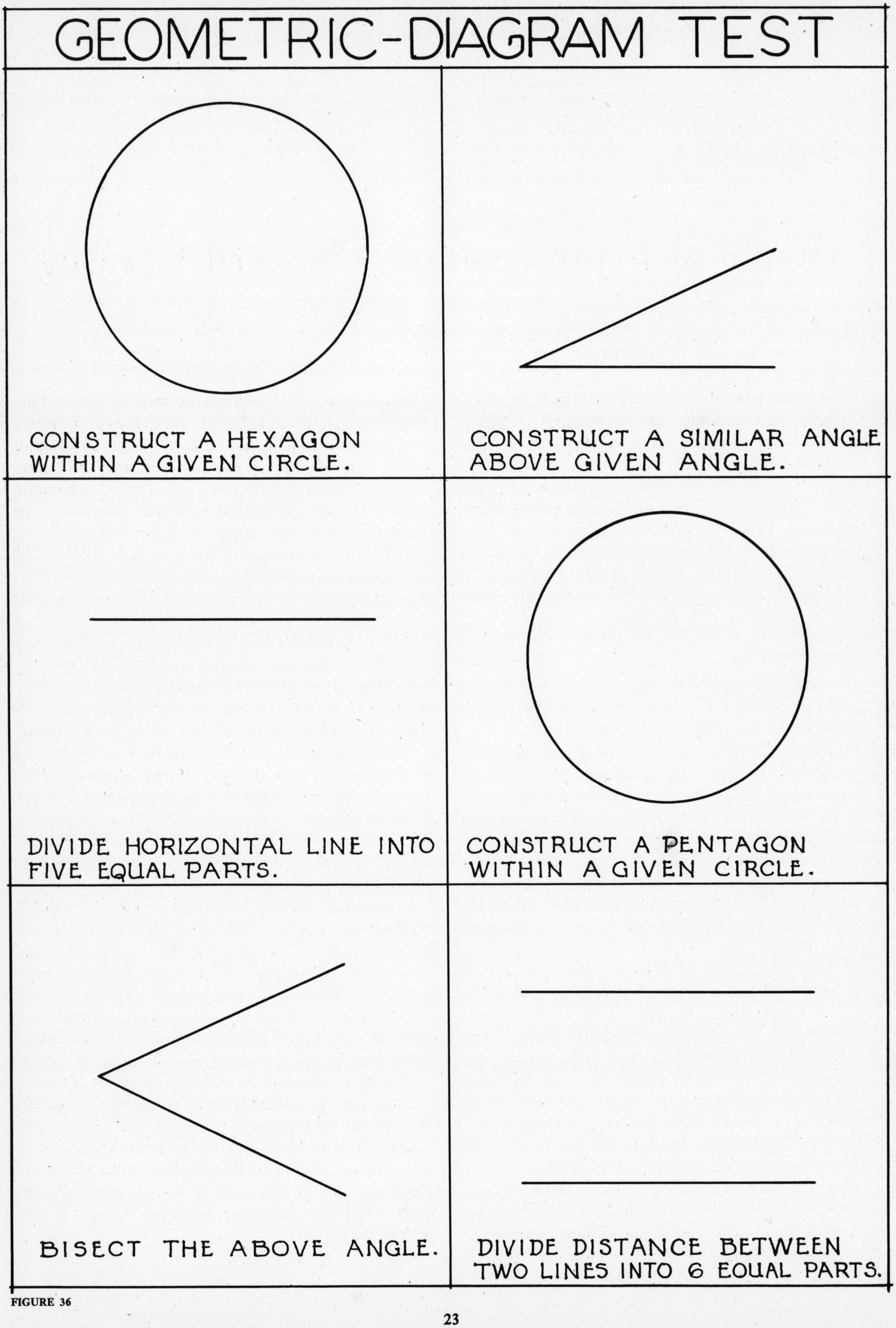

GEOMETRIC-DIAGRAM TEST

CONSTRUCT A HEXAGON
WITHIN A GIVEN CIRCLE.

CONSTRUCT A SIMILAR ANGLE
ABOVE GIVEN ANGLE.

DIVIDE HORIZONTAL LINE INTO
FIVE EQUAL PARTS.

CONSTRUCT A PENTAGON
WITHIN A GIVEN CIRCLE.

BISECT THE ABOVE ANGLE.

DIVIDE DISTANCE BETWEEN
TWO LINES INTO 6 EQUAL PARTS.

FIGURE 36

LESSON 4

Graphical Representation—Pictorial Drawing

The whole science or art of construction drawing is based on the assumption that the draftsman wants to *represent* some object so that another person can visualize that object and may take such dimensions and directions as may be necessary to reproduce the object itself. The object has three dimensions, length, width, and height. The draftsman represents the object on a sheet of paper that has only two dimensions, length and width. There are two general methods by which he does this: the first is called *pictorial drawing;* the second is *orthographic-projection drawing.*

Pictorial Drawing

Pictorial drawing may be classified according to three types, of which the general characteristics will be treated under the following headings.

1. Perspective drawing is the kind of representation everybody recognizes. This is the method always used by artists. It shows the object the way it appears, not the way it really is. For this reason, it is not suitable for working drawings. However, architects use it to make preliminary sketches or to show a client what a building will look like when finished. Perspective drawing is based on the optical illusion that makes railroad tracks appear to come together as they disappear in the distance.

It is not the purpose of this book to teach the intricate task of laying out a perspective drawing. Since the volume is primarily for beginners in drafting, it intends to show what a perspective drawing looks like and a few of the fundamental procedures used in developing such a drawing. If the student plans to study architectural design, a further study of perspective drawing will be necessary. However, every student of drafting should be able to sketch quickly in perspective those features of design that he cannot readily visualize himself.

The first items to be learned are the theory of perspective projection and the method used in presenting this projection. The student should think of an imaginary glass plate set up between the observer's eye and the object to be drawn. This is known as the *picture plane.* The front edge of the object should touch the picture plane, so that vertical measurements may be taken. The location of the observer's eye is called the *station point.* The vertical lines of the object, which rests on the ground line, will always be drawn vertically. All parallel lines on the object will meet at a point called the *vanishing point*, which is located on the horizon line. The horizon line is drawn parallel to the ground line and at eye level.

If the student will draw imaginary lines of sight from the station point through the picture plane to the corners of the plan and then connect the points where these lines cut through the picture plane, the result will be the perspective projection of the plan on the picture plane.

Notice that the projection of the plan on the picture plane is smaller than the plan because of the fact that the sight lines converge to the station point as they go from the plan to the picture plane. A perspective drawing is made to scale; but as it is only a pictorial drawing and not a working drawing, dimensions should not be scaled from it (see Fig. 37).

2. Isometric drawing. Because isometric drawing does not give a true picture of the object, the architect seldom uses it to illustrate a building. Instead, he uses perspective. There are times, however, when the architect uses an isometric drawing to make a picture of some intricate part of a detail in order to help the man in the shop visualize it more clearly. The stone sill of a door detail might be made in isometric to show the lugs on the ends and how the slope is made. Also, where there are complicated mechanical systems, engineers use isometric drawings of piping for plumbing and heating diagrams. In most cases, the wall and floors are imagined to have been removed, and only boilers, tanks, radiators, pipes, etc., are shown in their relationships to each other. Framing details are sometimes shown in isometric (see Fig. 51).

PICTORIAL DRAWINGS

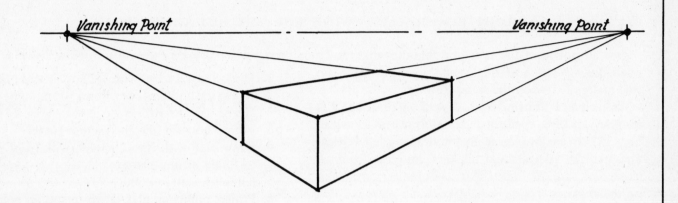

PERSPECTIVE: (a) Pictorial representation as object appears.
(b) All parallel lines converge at some distant point.

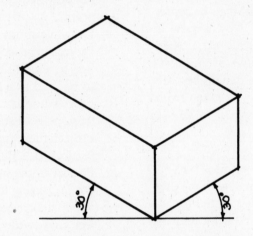

ISOMETRIC: (a) Vertical lines usually form axis and all other lines are drawn at 30° angle.
(b) All edges are made equal in size to object.

NOTE:
See Fig. #39 For Practical Examples of Pictoral Drwg's.

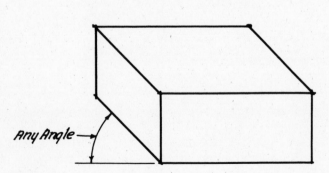

OBLIQUE: (a) All vertical lines remain vertical.
(b) All horizontal lines remain horizontal.
(c) Lines running from front to back are drawn at any desired angle.

FIGURE 37

One advantage of the method is that drawings can be made quickly with a 30° angle and showing both the top side and end view on the same drawing.

An isometric drawing is not a working drawing; it is only one of three types of pictorial drawings shown in Fig. 37. In making an isometric drawing, all vertical lines remain vertical, and all lines converge from an axis point at a 30° angle. All measurements are taken on the angle.

3. Oblique drawing, or cabinet perspective. Some objects, such as circular or irregular forms, are difficult to draw in isometric. These can be represented by oblique projections (see Fig. 37). To make an oblique drawing, the irregular face of the object should be parallel to the picture plane. This face can then be represented in scale exactly as it appears. Now a view is taken from one side and just above the object. Then the lines representing the sides are drawn at any convenient angle, usually 30 or 45°. The dimensions are kept to scale. If desired, the view may be taken from one side and just *below* the object.

PROBLEMS

1. Copy Fig. 37, using 9″ x 12″ sheet with ½″ border.

2. In order to gain some idea of the method of making a perspective drawing, the student should copy Fig. 38. All the various lines and points have been located by dimensions and should be drawn to actual size. In a sense, this is more an exercise in drafting than in perspective drawing, but the student will learn the method and can later practice making perspective sketches in freehand.

Procedure for Copying Perspective Drawing (See Fig. 38)

1. Use a 9″ x 12″ sheet with ½″ border and title box.
2. Draw ground line as shown from dimensions given.
3. Locate horizon line and picture plane.
4. Draw plan with 30-60° angles, with front corner touching picture plane.
5. Establish station point.
6. Project points on plan down to station point.
7. Using the same angles as on the plan, project lines from station point up to the picture plane. Where these points intersect the picture plane, drop lines down vertically until they touch the horizon line. These points will be the vanishing points.
8. Draw elevation to the right as shown.
9. Project front corner of plan down to the ground line to establish front corner of perspective and to be used as a measuring line.
10. Establish points on picture plane where lines from plan to station point cross.
11. Project these points down vertically to establish vertical lines on perspective.
12. Project horizontal lines across from elevation to the measuring line to establish heights.
13. From these heights on the measuring line, project lines to the vanishing points.
14. Where the lines going to the vanishing points intersect the vertical lines dropped down from the picture plane, the perspective can be completed.

PERSPECTIVE DRAWING

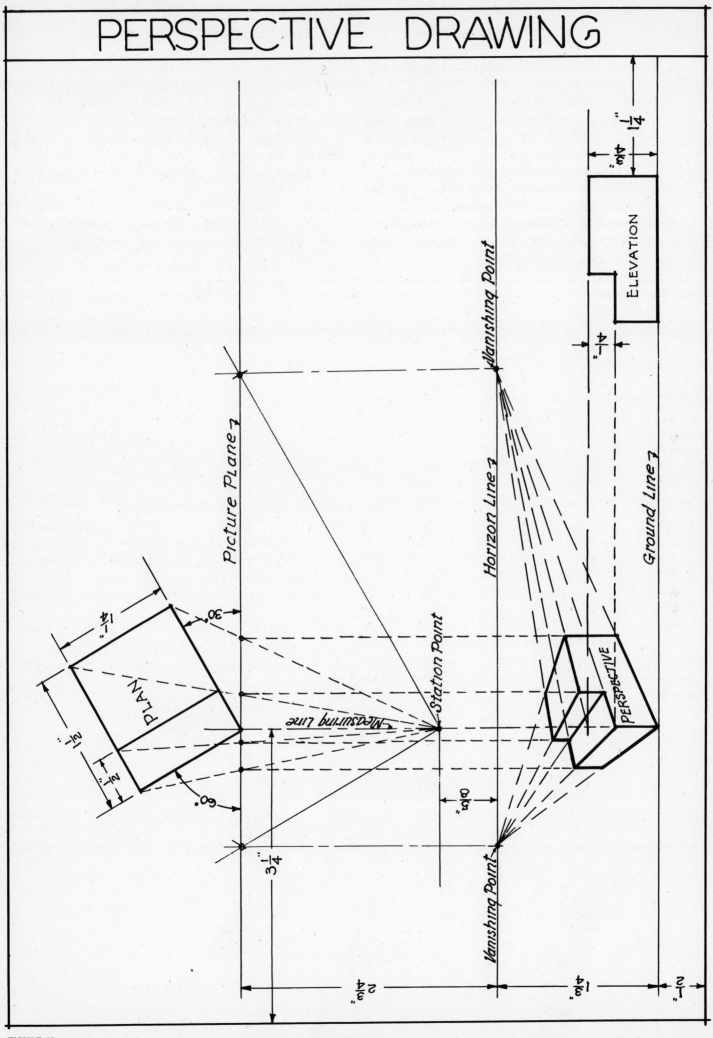

FIGURE 38

27

3. Procedure for copying isometric drawing (see Fig. 39).

1. Use a 12″ x 18″ sheet held vertically. Draw ½″ border line and title box. Divide sheet, using one half for this problem and the other for Prob. 4 on oblique drawing.
2. Draw solid isometric block with light lines.
3. Start with front vertical line as axis, and project back each side of line at 30° angle.
4. Measure true dimensions on these slopes and true height on vertical lines.

5. Complete the solid block. It is called the *crate*.
6. Using dimensions given, draw the block as shown, and erase parts of the solid block not used.
7. Put in all dimension lines and figures.

4. Procedure for copying oblique drawing of cabinet (see Fig. 39).

1. Draw lightly the outline of the entire cabinet from the dimensions given.
2. Show shelves and compartments.
3. Complete drawing, and erase all unnecessary lines.
4. Put in all dimension lines and figures.

ISOMETRIC & OBLIQUE DRAWING

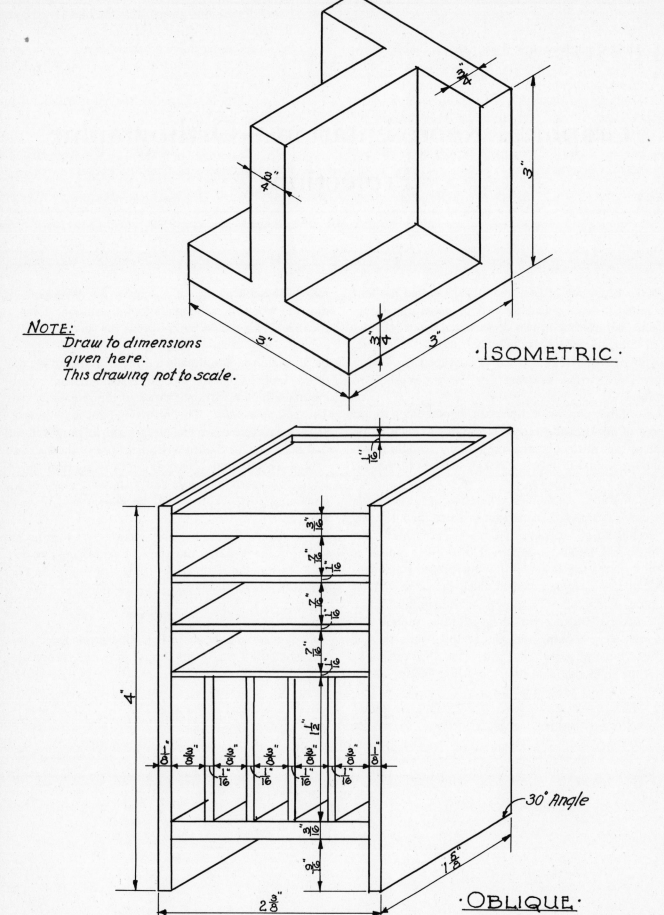

NOTE:
Draw to dimensions
given here.
This drawing not to scale.

·ISOMETRIC·

·OBLIQUE·

30° Angle

FIGURE 39

29

LESSON 5

Graphical Representation—Orthographic Projection

At the beginning of Lesson 4, it was pointed out that draftsmen have two general ways of presenting three-dimensional objects on two-dimensional paper: (1) pictorial drawing, which includes perspective, isometric, and oblique drawing; and (2) orthographic-projection drawing. Pictorial drawing has been discussed in Lesson 4.

An orthographic-projection drawing of a block would consist of one drawing as seen by looking straight at the front of the block, one drawing looking straight down at the top, and one drawing looking straight at the end of the block (see Fig. 40).

This method, sometimes referred to as *third-angle projection*, is standard American practice for all forms of architectural drawing, although occasionally an architectural detail is represented in first angle, a method now generally used only by foreign draftsmen.

A building is represented in much the same way as the block in Fig. 40. To show a building in third-angle projection, a drawing would be made as though the observer were looking straight at the front, then a drawing looking straight at the left side, then one looking at the right side, and then a drawing looking at the rear. These drawings are known as *elevations*. A drawing would then be made looking straight down at the top. This would be known as the *roof plan*.

Next, assume that a horizontal cut is made through the building along a line already indicated on the front elevation. Imagine that the top part is removed and a drawing made looking straight down at the remaining part. This is a *floor plan*. This horizontal cut may be taken at varying distances from the ground to show the second-floor plan or that of any other floor of the building.

Now assume that a vertical cut is made through the house, one part removed, and a drawing made of the remaining part. This would be known as a *sectional drawing*.

The plans, elevations, and sections go together to make up the working drawings of a building (see Fig. 40). In making a set of working drawings, the plan would be drawn first.

PROBLEM

Copy diagrams shown in Fig. 40, drawing three views and isometric first. Copy house drawings, proceeding as described above.

30

THIRD-ANGLE PROJECTION

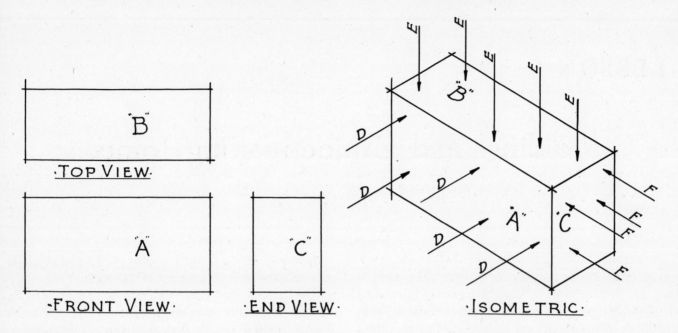

·TOP VIEW·

B̈

·FRONT VIEW·

Ä

·END VIEW·

C̈

·ISOMETRIC·

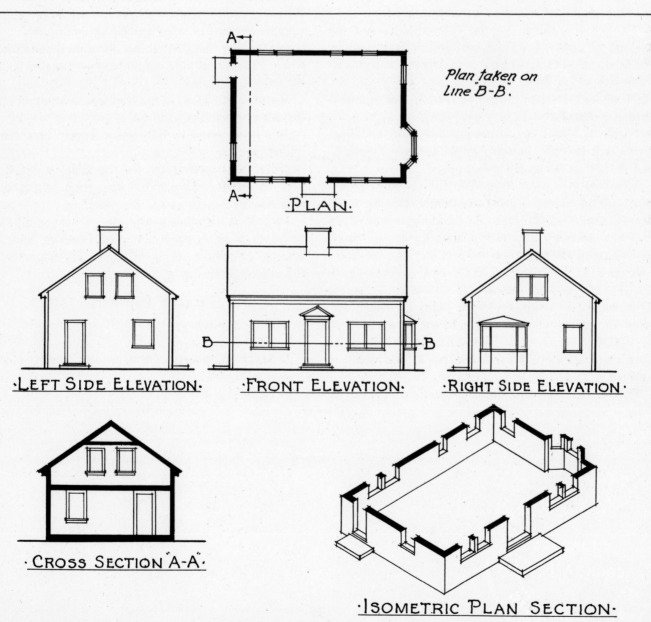

Plan taken on
Line "B-B".

·PLAN·

·LEFT SIDE ELEVATION·

·FRONT ELEVATION·

·RIGHT SIDE ELEVATION·

·CROSS SECTION "A-A"·

·ISOMETRIC PLAN SECTION·

FIGURE 40

31

LESSON 6

Moldings and Cabinetmaking Joints

The architect and the builder have always used moldings in one form or another for ornamental purposes. They are important as devices for creating interesting detail and design. The shadow patterns resulting from sunlight or reflected light on moldings are as important in the small home as in the most imposing edifice.

The nature of the design, the material to be used, the method of application, and cost are all factors to be considered in planning the use of moldings. The draftsman, builder, or architect to be will be well repaid for the time and study put into observation and examination of moldings.

Figure 41 shows the names and shapes of moldings considered as basic patterns in use today. Figure 42 shows how moldings are to be applied.

The draftsman must be familiar with the more important cabinet joints, for he frequently uses them in architectural details. Drawing these joints will afford excellent practice in careful draftsmanship and will assist in developing the technique and accuracy that prompt a mechanic to be equally careful and painstaking in carrying out the work indicated in the well-drawn plans. A cabinetmaker is known by the joints he makes, for carefully made joints not only enhance the appearance of a piece of furniture but also contribute largely to its strength and durability. Similarly, a draftsman is known by his technique and accuracy.

Following are descriptions of joints shown in Fig. 43.

Spliced or halved joint: The ends of two pieces joined in a continuous line to obtain extra length.

End-lap or halved joint: The end of one piece joins the end of another at an angle, for example, in screens, frames, small doors, or the panel type of construction. When the joint is made with a miter instead of being cut square across, it is called an *end-lap miter joint.*

Rabbet joint: Used in cabinet and drawer construction where a plain butt joint would be objectionable because of visible end grains.

Housed joint: Used in the back construction of drawers, for bookshelves, etc.

Butt joint: Used in box construction; often merely nailed together.

Miter with spline: Used for the stronger and better type of miter construction. The grain of the spline must run at right angles to the miter cut.

Through mortise and tenon joint: Used for all forms of frame or panel construction, as in doors, blinds, or screens. The hole portion is known as the *mortise* and the other part fitting into it as the *tenon.*

EXERCISES AND PROBLEMS

1. Copy Fig. 41.
2. Copy Fig. 42.
3. Make up a sheet of cornice molds, applying figures shown in Fig. 41.
4. Copy Fig. 43.

MOLDINGS

NOTE: See Fig.#42 For Moldings Applied

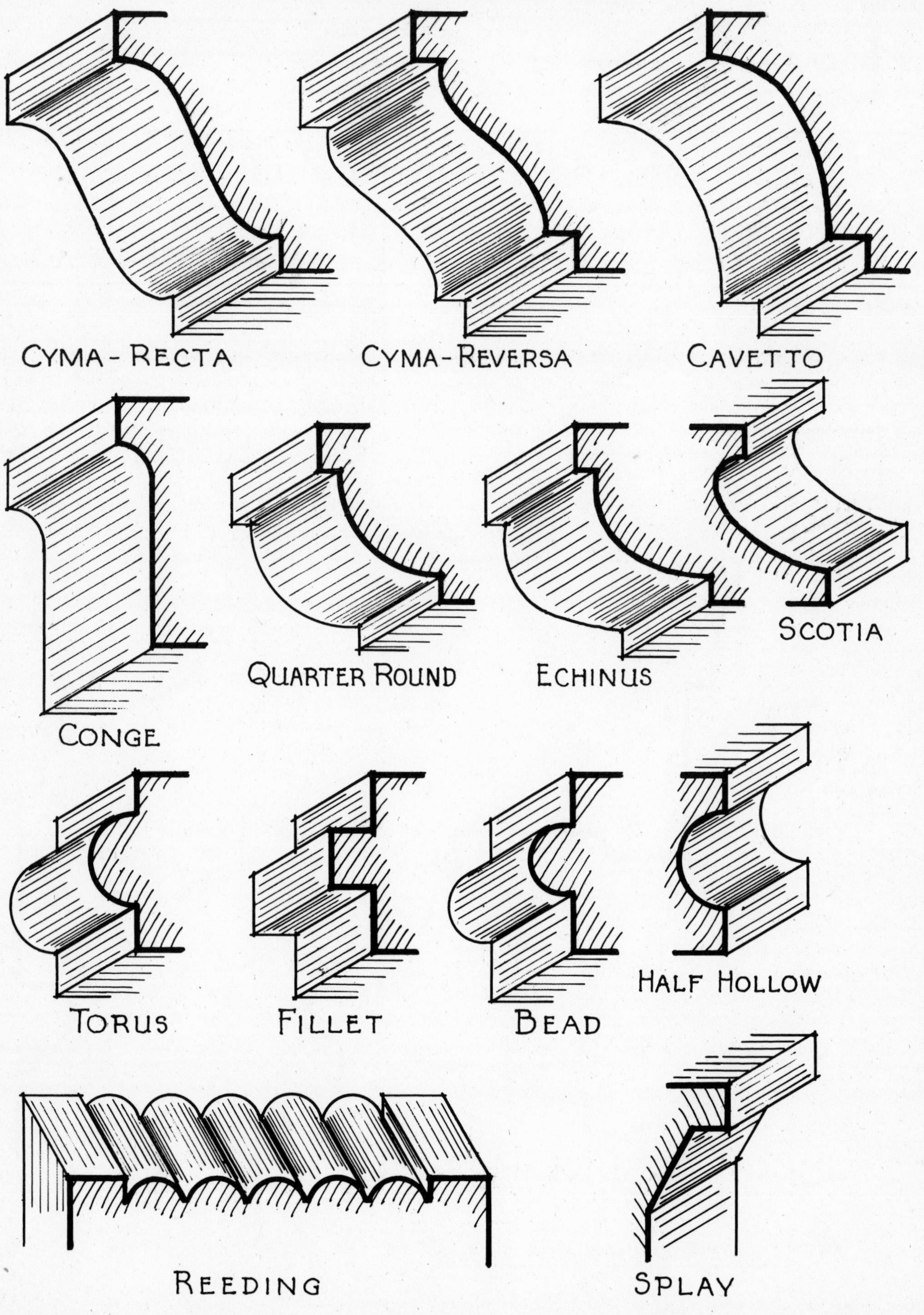

CYMA - RECTA

CYMA - REVERSA

CAVETTO

CONGE

QUARTER ROUND

ECHINUS

SCOTIA

TORUS

FILLET

BEAD

HALF HOLLOW

REEDING

SPLAY

FIGURE 41

MOLDINGS APPLIED

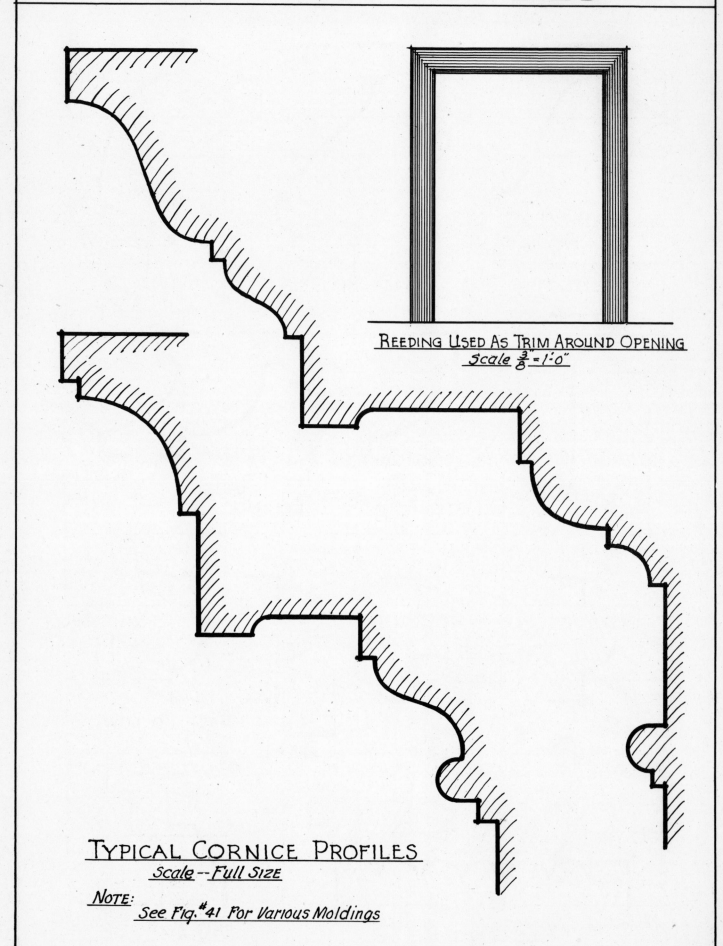

REEDING USED AS TRIM AROUND OPENING
Scale $\frac{3}{8}" = 1'-0"$

TYPICAL CORNICE PROFILES
Scale -- Full Size

NOTE:
See Fig.#41 For Various Moldings

FIGURE 42

34

CABINETMAKING JOINTS

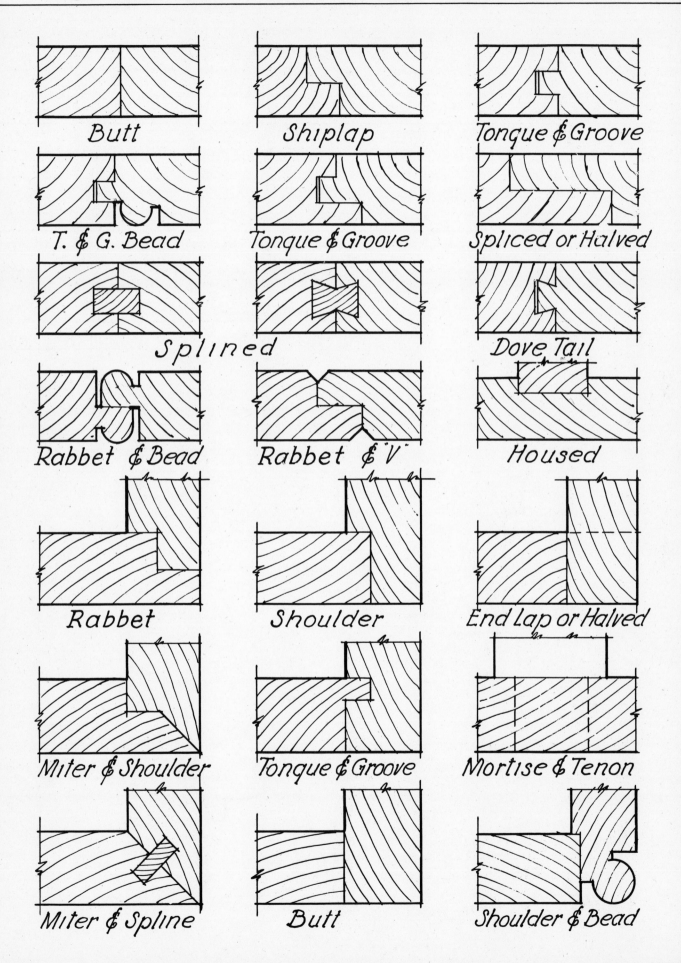

Butt	Shiplap	Tonque & Groove
T. & G. Bead	Tonque & Groove	Spliced or Halved
Splined		Dove Tail
Rabbet & Bead	Rabbet & "V"	Housed
Rabbet	Shoulder	End Lap or Halved
Miter & Shoulder	Tonque & Groove	Mortise & Tenon
Miter & Spline	Butt	Shoulder & Bead

FIGURE 43

35

LESSON 7

Symbols, Schedules, and Conventions

SYMBOLS

Symbols are the shorthand outlines of draftsmen. Most of them have been standardized through common use. Occasionally an architect who specializes in one particular type of work has his own symbols, which will be shown usually in the key to materials on the first-floor plan.

This fact prompts the suggestion that the good draftsman should be able to read working drawings speedily. A good set of working drawings together with the specifications describe a building thoroughly. Practice in reading many of these will help the student visualize buildings and will give him an opportunity to pick up tricks of the trade, short cuts, and methods by which he can improve his work. In the making of a good draftsman, the next best thing to drawing is the ability to read good drawings.

Figure 44 shows some commonly accepted architectural symbols. Figure 45 shows plumbing, heating, and electrical symbols.

SCHEDULES

A schedule is a systematic method of presenting notes on a drawing in tabular form for the purpose of making easily accessible to the craftsman and specification writer the detailed information they require. A door schedule would show the type, style, description, and location of each door. A window schedule would give the same information regarding windows. A finish schedule showing the kind of finish for floors, walls, ceilings, trim, etc., for each room on a floor plan is particularly important. There are also schedules on concrete and steel-beam lintels, columns, and footings.

Of course, all this information may be found in the specifications on any particular piece of construction, but the workman is not handling the specifications all the time, whereas he does have constant access to the working drawings. Therefore, the essential information that he requires at all times in order to carry out his assignment perfectly is presented in this clear, concise, and accurate manner. The necessity of good lettering in scheduling is obvious.

Figure 46 shows typical schedules.

CONVENTIONS

Conventions are still another form of draftsman's shorthand. They are standardized and commonly accepted methods by which an architect presents given facts. Some of the principal conventions used by architects in working drawings are shown in Fig. 47. To be a good draftsman, it is necessary to memorize symbols and conventions and to practice drawing them from memory. Study as many working drawings as possible so as to become thoroughly familiar with all types of symbols, conventions, schedules, and other notations.

Concrete foundation walls and solid brick walls are dimensioned to the outside corner because they line up with each other.

Brick-veneer walls are dimensioned to the outside face of the wood frame because the frame is built complete before the brick veneer is applied. Wood-stud walls are dimensioned to rough frame because boarding and siding are applied after the frame is in place, as shown in Fig. 47.

Wood studs in interior walls are dimensioned to the center of the studs because of the variation in the size of studs. All rough framework such as studs, floor joists, and rafters is dimensioned from center to center.

Interior masonry walls are dimensioned to the face of the wall.

Doors and windows are dimensioned to the center line because the frames are made up first and set into the rough opening.

PROBLEMS

1. Copy Fig. 44.
2. Copy Fig. 45.
3. Copy Fig. 46.
4. Copy Fig. 47.

ARCHITECTURAL SYMBOLS

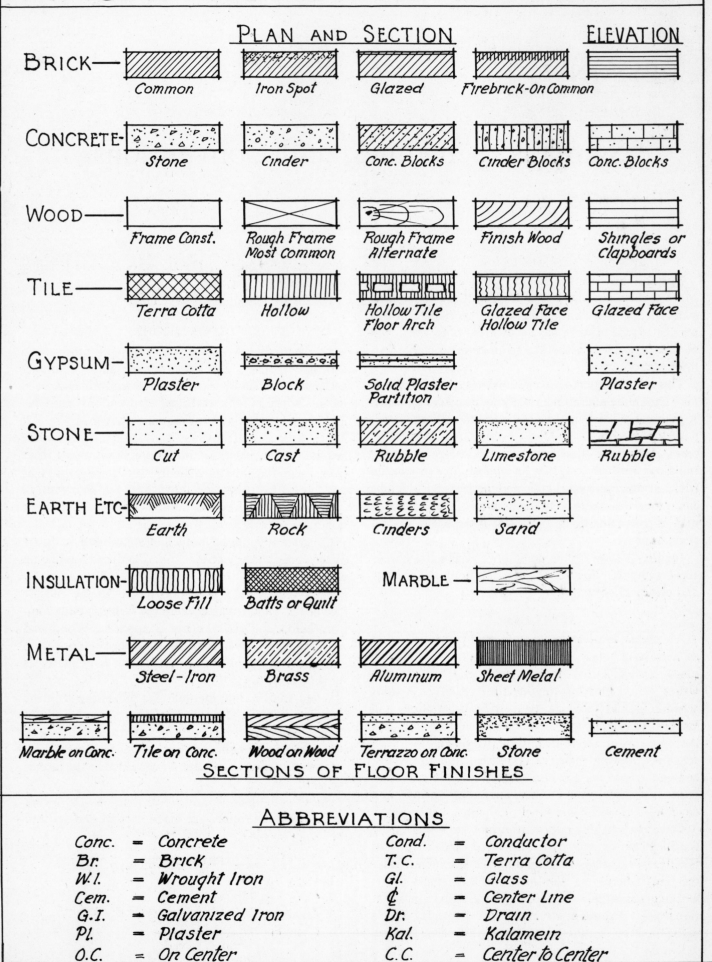

PLAN AND SECTION · ELEVATION

BRICK — Common · Iron Spot · Glazed · Firebrick-on Common

CONCRETE — Stone · Cinder · Conc. Blocks · Cinder Blocks · Conc. Blocks

WOOD — Frame Const. · Rough Frame Most Common · Rough Frame Alternate · Finish Wood · Shingles or Clapboards

TILE — Terra Cotta · Hollow · Hollow Tile Floor Arch · Glazed Face Hollow Tile · Glazed Face

GYPSUM — Plaster · Block · Solid Plaster Partition · Plaster

STONE — Cut · Cast · Rubble · Limestone · Rubble

EARTH ETC — Earth · Rock · Cinders · Sand

INSULATION — Loose Fill · Batts or Quilt · MARBLE —

METAL — Steel-Iron · Brass · Aluminum · Sheet Metal

Marble on Conc. · Tile on Conc. · Wood on Wood · Terrazzo on Conc. · Stone · Cement

SECTIONS OF FLOOR FINISHES

ABBREVIATIONS

Conc.	=	Concrete	Cond.	=	Conductor
Br.	=	Brick	T.C.	=	Terra Cotta
W.I.	=	Wrought Iron	Gl.	=	Glass
Cem.	=	Cement	₵	=	Center Line
G.I.	=	Galvanized Iron	Dr.	=	Drain
Pl.	=	Plaster	Kal.	=	Kalamein
O.C.	=	On Center	C.C.	=	Center to Center

FIGURE 44

38

MECHANICAL SYMBOLS

· PLUMBING · SYMBOLS ·

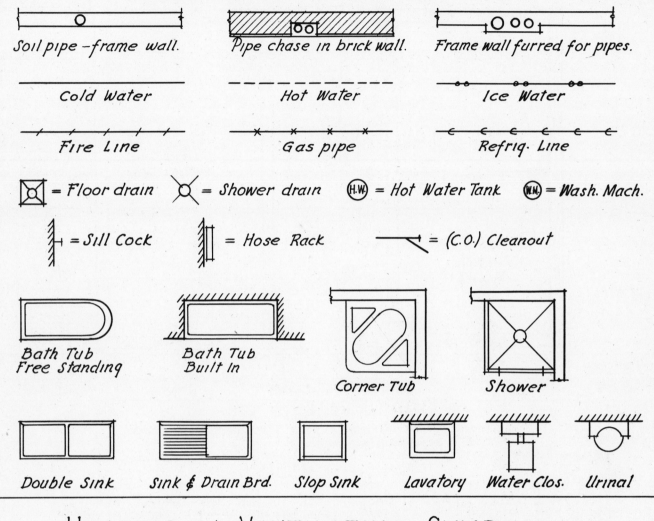

Soil pipe – frame wall. Pipe chase in brick wall. Frame wall furred for pipes.

Cold Water Hot Water Ice Water

Fire Line Gas pipe Refrig. Line

= Floor drain = Shower drain (H.W) = Hot Water Tank (W.M.) = Wash. Mach.

= Sill Cock = Hose Rack = (C.O.) Cleanout

Bath Tub Free Standing Bath Tub Built In Corner Tub Shower

Double Sink Sink & Drain Brd. Slop Sink Lavatory Water Clos. Urinal

· HEATING · and · VENTILATING · SYMBOLS ·

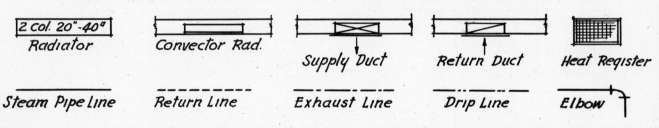

2 Col. 20"-40"
Radiator Convector Rad. Supply Duct Return Duct Heat Register

Steam Pipe Line Return Line Exhaust Line Drip Line Elbow

· ELECTRICAL · SYMBOLS ·

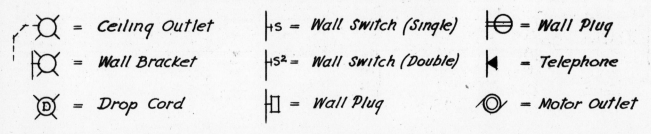

= Ceiling Outlet $\vdash$S = Wall Switch (Single) = Wall Plug

= Wall Bracket $\vdash$S² = Wall Switch (Double) = Telephone

(D) = Drop Cord = Wall Plug = Motor Outlet

FIGURE 45

39

SCHEDULES

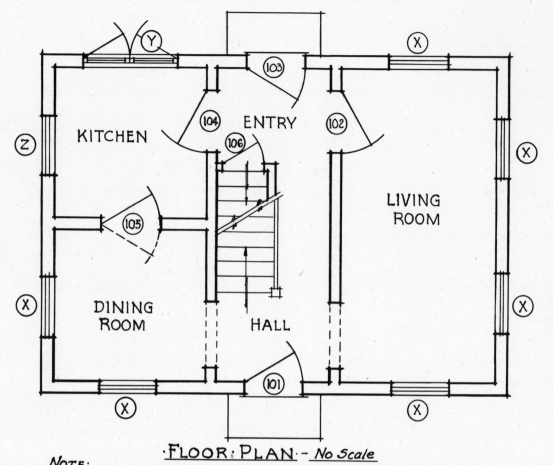

·FLOOR·PLAN· – *No Scale*

N<small>OTE</small>: *This is an outline plan only to show how schedules are used. It is not a working drawing.*

·FINISH SCHEDULE·

ROOM	WALLS	DADO	BASE	FLOOR	CEILING	CORNICE	REMARKS
LIV. ROOM	Plaster	Canvas	Wood	Oak	Plaster	Wood	Special Trim
DIN. ROOM	"	"	"	"	"	Pict. Mold.	Cupbd.
KITCHEN	"	4'-0" Tile	Tile	Linoleum	"		
HALL	"		Wood	Oak	"	Wood	See Detail
ENTRY	"		"	Linoleum	"		

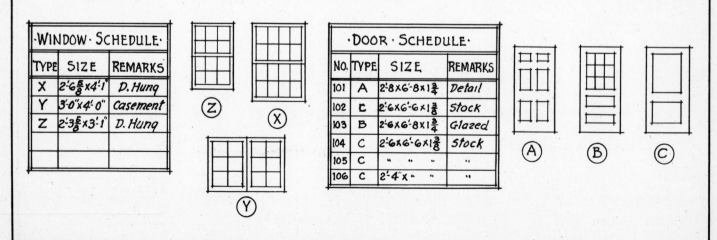

·WINDOW·SCHEDULE·

TYPE	SIZE	REMARKS
X	2'-6⅝"x4'-1"	D. Hung
Y	3'-0"x4'-0"	Casement
Z	2'-3⅝"x3'-1"	D. Hung

·DOOR·SCHEDULE·

NO.	TYPE	SIZE	REMARKS
101	A	2'-8x6'-8x1¾	Detail
102	C	2'-6x6'-6x1⅜	Stock
103	B	2'-6x6'-8x1¾	Glazed
104	C	2'-6x6'-6x1⅜	Stock
105	C	" " "	"
106	C	2'-4"x " "	"

FIGURE 46

40

CONVENTIONS

NOTE: Dimension to ¢ of all doors and windows unless otherwise shown.

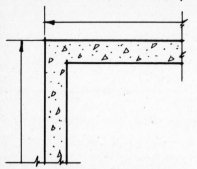
Concrete Wall (Dimension to Outside Corner.)

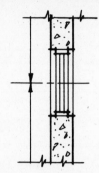
Double-Hung Wood Window.

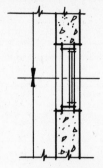
Hinged Wood Cellar Window.

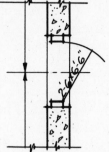
Exterior Door.

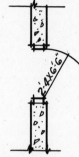
Interior Door.

·CONCRETE WALL INDICATIONS·

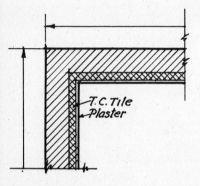
Solid Brick Wall (Dimension to Outside Corner)

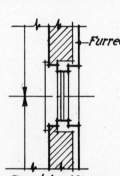
Double-Hung Wood Window.

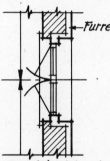
Double Wood Casement.

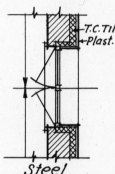
Steel Casement.

·SOLID BRICK WALL INDICATIONS·

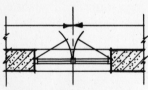
Metal Casement Conc. Block Wall.

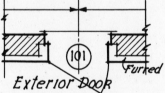
Exterior Door Solid Brick Wall.

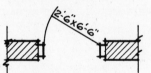
Interior Door Solid Brick Wall.

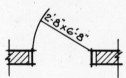
Interior Door T. C. Tile Wall.

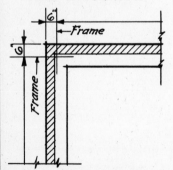
Brick Veneer Wall Dim. to Wood Frame.

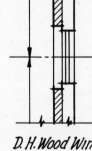
D. H. Wood Window In Brick Veneer.

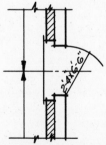
Exterior Door Brick Veneer.

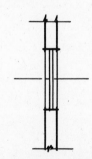
D.H. Wood Window In Wood Frame.

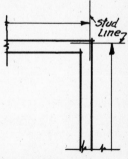
Wood Frame Dim. to Studs.

D.H. Mullion Window In Wood Frame Wall.

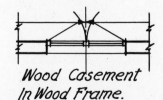
Wood Casement In Wood Frame.

Exterior Door In Wood Frame.

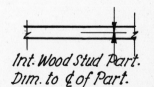
Int. Wood Stud Part. Dim. to ¢ of Part.

FIGURE 47

41

LESSON 8

Concrete-wall Indications

The purpose of this and the following two lessons is to familiarize the student with the various symbols and conventions by actually drawing them to scale. The diagrams shown are outlines of imaginary plans of houses, showing the wall outline, with center lines indicating the location of different types of windows and doors.

It will be necessary to refer frequently to the symbol and convention sheets to obtain the proper indication for wall materials and for the openings called for in these diagrams.

PROBLEM BASED ON FIG. 48

1. Use 9″ x 12″ sheet with ½″ border and title box.
2. Using ¼″ = 1′-0″ scale, lightly draw the outside line of entire diagram from the dimensions given.
3. Draw the inside-wall line (refer to Fig. 13 for correct weight of lines).

4. Locate center lines of all openings from dimensions given.
5. Draw in the proper indications (see Fig. 47) for all door and window openings, using the following dimensions:
   a. Masonry openings for all windows—2′-10″ wide.
   b. Masonry openings for all doors in outside walls—3′-4″ wide.
6. Draw all extension lines, and add dimension lines with neat arrowheads as indicated (see Fig. 47 for dimensioning).
7. All vertical dimensions read from the bottom to the top of the sheet and from the right.
8. Put in dimensions wherever indicated in diagram.
9. Indicate material called for (refer to Fig. 44).
10. Go over outline of wall with firm, clean line (refer again to Fig. 13).

WALL INDICATIONS

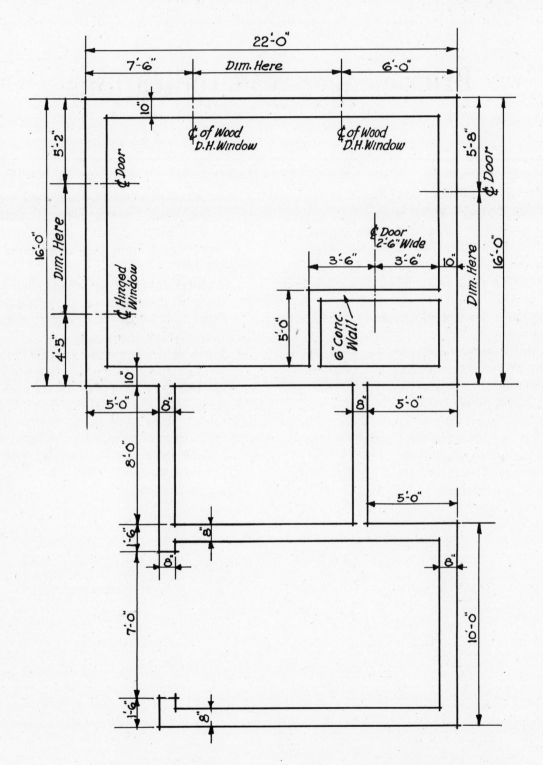

·CONCRETE·WALL·INDICATIONS·

This is a diagram only for
practice drawing.
This drawing is not drawn to scale.
See Text.

FIGURE 48

43

LESSON 9

Brick-veneer-wall Indications

PROBLEM BASED ON FIG. 49

1. Use 9″ x 12″ paper with ½″ border and title box.
2. Using ¼″ = 1′-0″ scale, lightly draw the outside line of entire diagram from the dimensions given.
3. Draw inside-plaster-wall line (see Fig. 47).
4. Show line of wood frame 6″ in from brick line (see Fig. 47).
5. Locate center lines of all openings from dimensions given.
6. Draw in the proper indications (see Fig. 47) for all door and window openings, using the following dimensions for masonry openings:
   a. All double-hung windows to be 3′-0″ wide.
   b. All single wood casement windows 2′-6″ wide.
   c. All double wood casement windows to be 4′-0″ wide.
   d. All double-hung mullion windows to be 5′-0″ wide.
   e. All doors to be 3′-4″ wide.
7. Show all dimension and extension lines as indicated. Note that the figures go to the stud line in wood-frame construction.
8. Put in dimensions where indicated in diagram.
9. Indicate material called for (refer to Fig. 44).
10. Go over outline of wall with a firm, clean line (refer again to Fig. 13).

WALL INDICATIONS

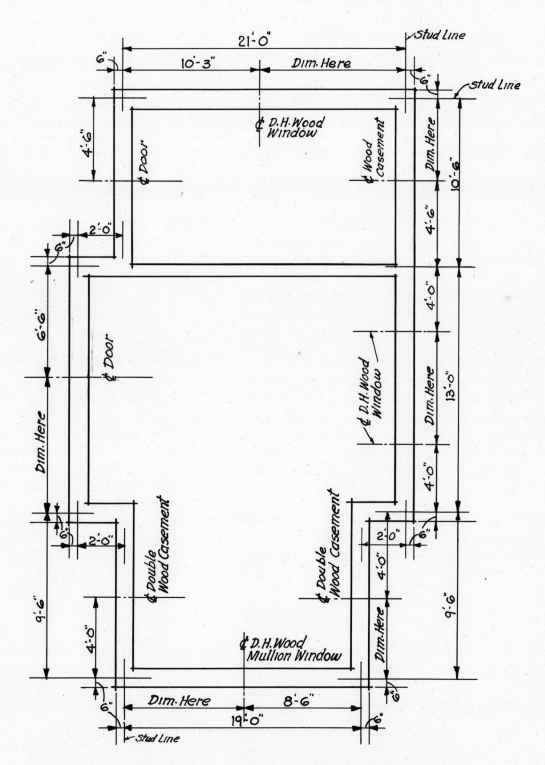

·BRICK·VENEER·WALL·INDICATIONS·

This is a diagram only for
practice drawing.
This drawing is not drawn to scale.
See Text.

FIGURE 49

45

LESSON 10

Solid-brick- and Wood-frame-construction Indications

PROBLEM BASED ON FIG. 50

1. Use 12″ x 18″ paper with ½″ border and title box.
2. Using ¼″ = 1′-0″ scale, lightly draw the outside line of entire diagram from dimensions given. Use 30-60° triangle for drawing angle of wood-frame construction. All corners are at right angles.
3. Draw the inside line of the brick wall, referring to diagram for thickness of wall.
4. Draw inside plaster line and interior partitions. Make all exterior wood-frame walls 6″ thick. Interior wood-stud walls are 5½″ thick. The furring on the inside of the brick walls consists of 2″ x 3″ studs laid flatwise with lath and plaster applied. For drafting purposes, this distance will be 3″ from the inside face of the brick to the finished plaster line.
5. Locate center line of all openings from dimensions given.
6. Draw in proper indications (see Fig. 47) for all doors and windows. Garage doors consist of two 4′-0″ doors, which swing out. They are indicated the same as a typical door in wood-frame construction. The following figures are to be used for masonry openings in the brick wall:
   a. All double-hung windows to be 3′-2″ wide.
   b. All double steel casement windows to be 4′-2″ wide.
   c. All doors to be 3′-4″ wide.
   For openings in wood-frame walls, use the following figures:
   a. All double-hung wood windows to be 2′-8″ wide.
   b. All single wood casement windows 2′-4″ wide.
   c. All doors to be 3′-0″ wide.
7. Show all dimension and extension lines as indicated. Note that dimensions go to the stud line in wood-frame construction.
8. Put in dimensions where indicated in diagram.
9. Indicate material called for (refer to Fig. 44).
10. Go over outline of wall with a firm, clean line (refer again to Fig. 13).

WALL INDICATIONS

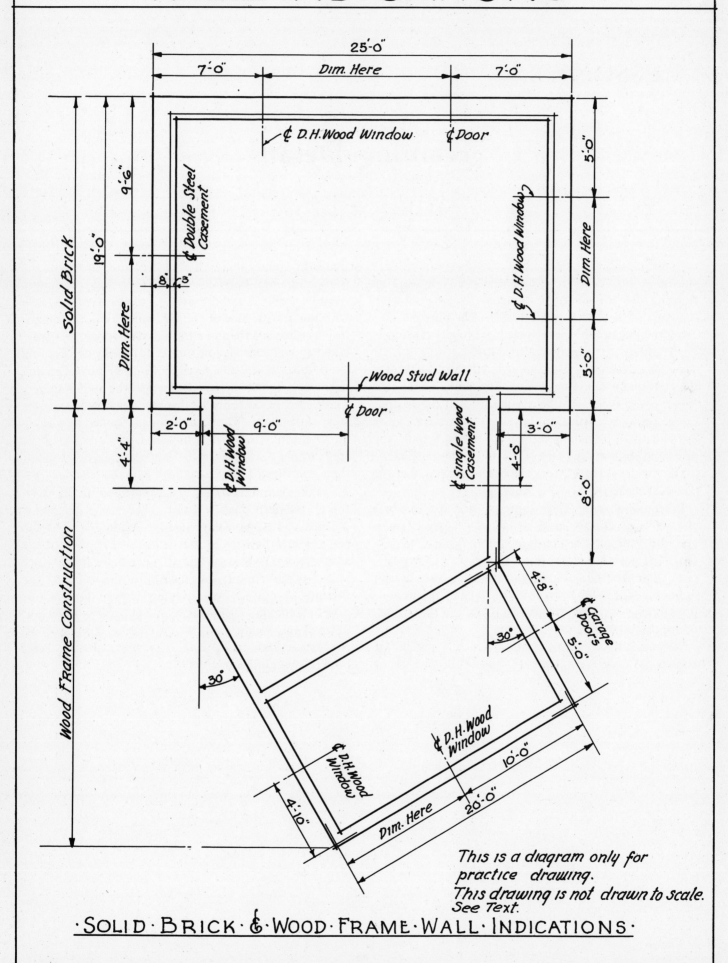

This is a diagram only for practice drawing.
This drawing is not drawn to scale.
See Text.

· S O L I D · B R I C K · & · W O O D · F R A M E · W A L L · I N D I C A T I O N S ·

FIGURE 50

47

LESSON 11

Framing Details

There are different kinds of framing, two of which are shown in Fig. 51. Note that this is not a working drawing but is a pictorial isometric drawing showing the corner frame of a small house. The purpose is to show how the frame is constructed and to give the names of the different parts of the framework.

Balloon Framing. The characteristic of this frame is the continuous studding from sill to plate. A 1″ x 6″ ledger board is set into the outside studs at the second-floor level to carry the floor joists. The first-floor joists are sometimes placed directly on the masonry walls, the posts and studs resting on a 4″ x 4″ sill laid on top of the joist. In the cheapest work the braces are omitted, the diagonal sheathing bracing the framing.

Braced Framing. This frame is used for the best class of work and for large buildings. It is very rigid, and the wall girts prevent the rapid spread of fire. Girts and posts are mortised together. After sill, posts, girts, plate, and braces are framed up, the studs are set in place. The drop girt is lowered to carry the second-floor joists. A raised girt is flush on top with the second-floor joists to receive the flooring.

There is a third type of framing, which is not shown, known as *western* or *platform frame*. In western or platform frame a 2″ x 8″ sill is placed on top of the foundation wall on which a 2″ x 8″ or 2″ x 10″ header is set edgewise. The outside face of the header is flush with the outside face of the sill, leaving a ledge on the inside to receive the floor joists. The rough flooring is laid diagonally on the joists, on top of the rough flooring a modified sill, or "sole piece," of 2″ x 4″ is laid flat, and to this the lower end of each exterior wall stud is spiked. These studs extend only the height of the first floor in this style of framing. The second floor is framed by placing girts made of two 2″ x 4″ beams set flatwise on top of the studs with a 2″ x 8″ or 2″ x 10″ joist set edgewise on top of them, the outside face being flush with the outside of the 2″ x 4″ beams, and leaving a ledge of about 2″ on which the second-floor joists will rest. The rough flooring is nailed diagonally on these joists. Again a 2″ x 4″ sole piece is laid flatwise to receive the lower ends of the second-story wall studding. Diagonal braces are nailed in between the studs near the corners on both the first and second stories. Detailed descriptions of this type of framing, which has become popular in some sections of the country and which enables the builder to cut costs on framing material, may be found in any good book on building construction.

FRAMING DETAILS

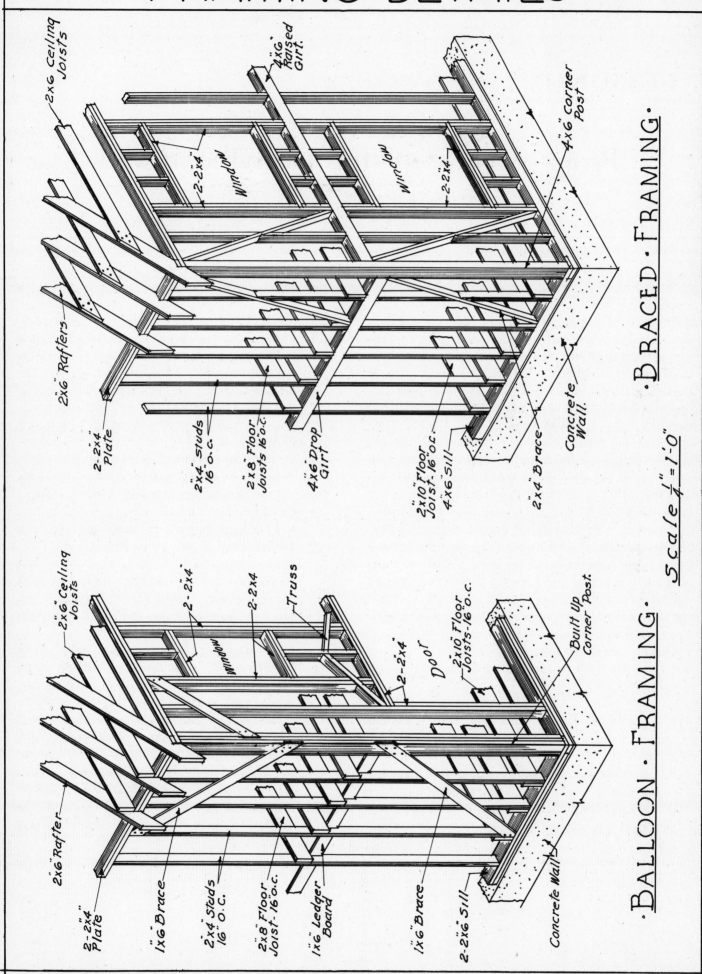

2x6 Ceiling Joists

4x6 Raised Girt.

4x6 Corner Post

2-2x4"

Window

Window

2-2x4"

2x6" Rafters

2-2x4" Plate

2x4" studs 16" o.c.

2x8" Floor Joists 16" o.c.

4x6 Drop Girt

2x10" Floor Joist-16" o.c.

4x6 Sill

2x4" Brace

Concrete Wall.

·BRACED·FRAMING·

Scale 1/4"=1'-0"

2x6 Ceiling joists

2-2x4

2-2x4

Truss

Window

Door

2-2x4

2x10 Floor Joists-16" o.c.

Built Up Corner Post.

2x6" Rafter

2-2x4" Plate

1x6" Brace

2x4" Studs 16" O.C.

2x8" Floor Joist-16" o.c.

1x6" Ledger Board

1x6" Brace

2-2x6" Sill

Concrete Wall

·BALLOON·FRAMING·

FIGURE 51

49

LESSON 12

Progressive Steps for Drawing Details
of Sill Construction

Every set of working drawings includes construction details. Construction details are large-scale or full-size working drawings showing the important parts of a building that are difficult to show clearly or accurately on the small-scale drawings. For the most part they are sectional drawings showing the construction behind the surface.

In planning details of any part of a building, the first step always is to ascertain the conditions and the limitations "to work to." Then the draftsman starts his drawing.

Based on Fig. 52, the student will follow the step-by-step procedure in drawing sill details for wood, brick-veneer, and solid brick construction. In drawing these details, all wood construction should be drawn the actual size in which the lumber comes to the job, and not as noted on the drawing. All lumber is planed at the mill, reducing its size about ⅛″ on all four surfaces. Thus, a 2″ x 4″ stud would actually be only 1¾″ x 3¾″ when delivered to the job.

PROBLEM 1. WOOD-FRAME CONSTRUCTION (see Fig. 52)

1. Use 9″ x 12″ sheet held vertically, with ½″ border and title box.
2. Draw Step 3 only at 1½″ scale.
3. Determine thickness of foundation wall, and draw top part as shown. Only a small portion of the wall need be indicated. Cut off with a broken line, as it is not necessary to show a complete wall (see Fig. 52).

4. *a.* Draw the sill, taking care that it is shown to be 1″ back from the outside face of the wall so that the boarding will be flush with the face of the foundation wall. Thus, the siding or water table will cover the joint where the boarding and concrete wall meet.
   b. Draw in 2″ x 4″ upright studs flush with the sill on the outside.
   c. Draw in the boarding.
   d. Draw the floor joists resting on the sill as shown. (In some cases, the floor joist is notched out at the sill to make all the joists even at the top. Consult framing plans to determine which way the joists run.)

5. *a.* Draw siding and water table as shown. This detail may vary considerably, depending upon design and the material used for outside finish.
   b. Draw in the rough floor, running it through to the inside face of the studs.
   c. Show the plaster line and grounds behind the baseboard. This is always ¾″ thick unless special conditions require another dimension.
   d. Draw in the baseboard, carrying it down to the rough floor. Baseboard is nailed into grounds.
   e. Draw in the finished floor. Show anchor bolts. These should be approximately 8′-0″ o.c. placed in the concrete wall as it is being built.
   f. Indicate materials by proper symbols and notes (see Fig. 44).
   g. All dimensioning and lettering should be put in last.

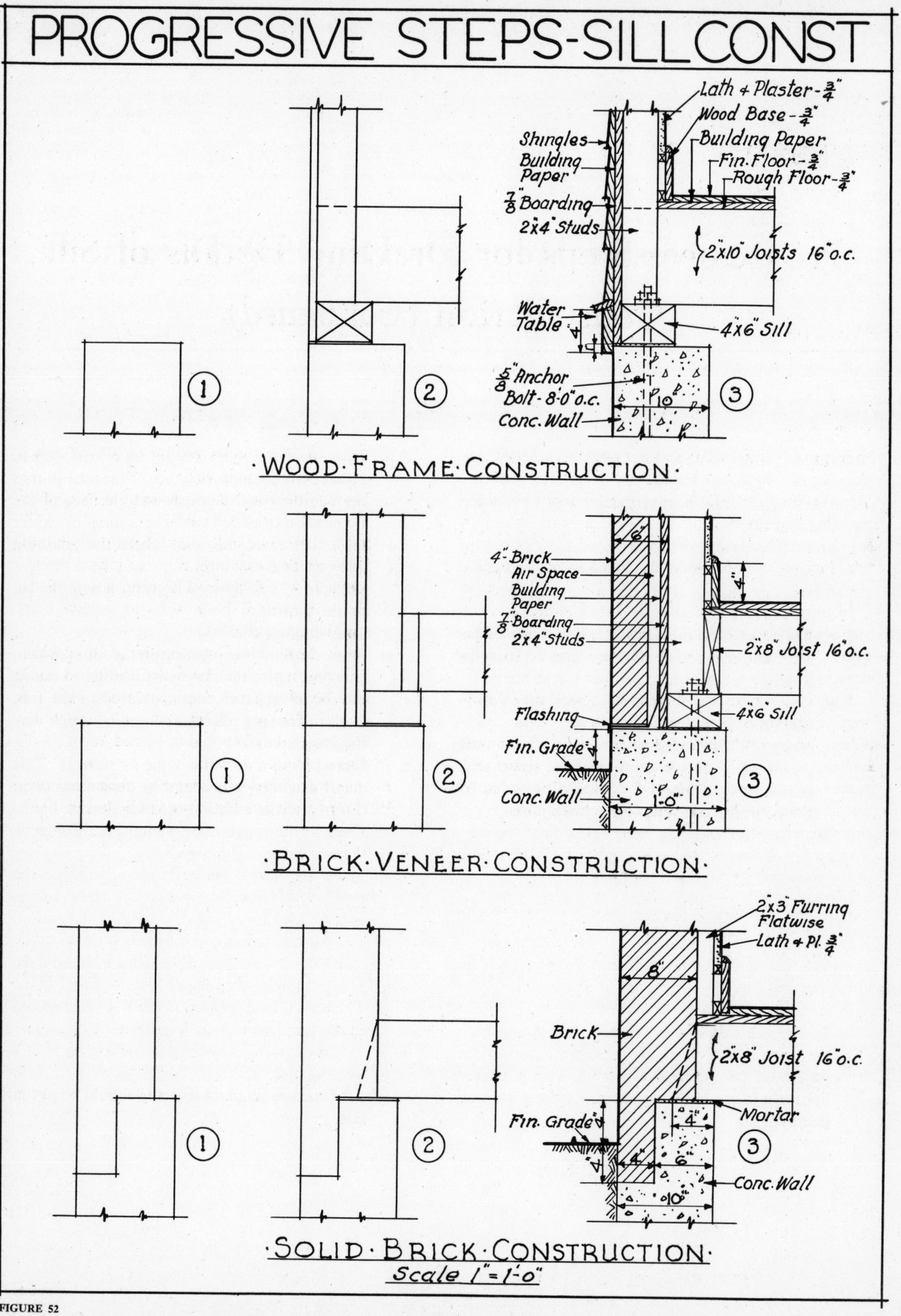

PROGRESSIVE STEPS-SILL CONST

Lath & Plaster-¾"
Wood Base-¾"
Building Paper
Fin. Floor-¾"
Rough Floor-¾"
Shingles
Building Paper
⅞" Boarding
2"x4" Studs
2"x10" Joists 16" o.c.
Water Table
4"x6" Sill
⅝" Anchor Bolt- 8'-0" o.c.
Conc. Wall
10"

① ② ③

·WOOD·FRAME·CONSTRUCTION·

4" Brick
Air Space
Building Paper
⅞" Boarding
2"x4" Studs
6"
4"
2"x8" Joist 16" o.c.
Flashing
4"x6" Sill
Fin. Grade
Conc. Wall
1'-0"

① ② ③

·BRICK·VENEER·CONSTRUCTION·

2"x3" Furring Flatwise
Lath & Pl. ¾"
8"
Brick
2"x8" Joist 16" o.c.
Mortar
Fin. Grade
4"
4" 6"
Conc. Wall
10"

① ② ③

·SOLID·BRICK·CONSTRUCTION·
Scale 1"=1'-0"

FIGURE 52

51

LESSON 13

Progressive Steps for Drawing Details of Sill Construction *(Continued)*

PROBLEM 2. BRICK-VENEER CONSTRUCTION (see Fig. 52)

1. Use 9″ x 12″ sheet held vertically, with ½″ border line and title box.
2. Draw Step 3 only at 1½″ scale.
3. Determine thickness of foundation wall, and draw top part as shown. Indicate only a small portion of the wall.
4. *a.* Locate sill 6″ in from the face of the foundation wall, and indicate as shown. This 6″ space is to allow for boarding, air space, and brick.

   b. Draw 2″ x 4″ wall studs flush with sill on outside, and show boarding on studs.

   c. Indicate 4″ brick wall flush with foundation wall on outside. This is known as *brick veneer* and is tied to the framing by metal clips nailed to the boarding and set into the brick joists.

d. Draw the floor joists resting on sill as shown (see Lesson 12, Step 4*d*).

5. *a.* Draw in the rough floor, running it through to the inside face of the studs.

   b. Show plaster line and grounds behind baseboard.

   c. Draw in the baseboard, carrying it down to the rough floor. Baseboard is nailed into grounds.

   d. Draw in finished floor, showing anchor bolts approximately 8′-0″ o.c.

   e. Show flashing at intersection of brickwork. This flashing should be nailed to the boarding with building paper lapping over the joint. It should then run down and out through the bottom joint and should be turned down on the outside face of the wall.

   f. Indicate materials by proper symbols and notes.

   g. Dimensioning and lettering should be put in last.

LESSON 14

Progressive Steps for Drawing Details of Sill Construction *(Continued)*

PROBLEM 3. SOLID BRICK CONSTRUCTION (see Fig. 52)

1. Use 9″ x 12″ sheet held vertically, with ½″ border and title box.
2. Draw Step 3 only at 1½″ scale.
3. Before starting the drawing of the foundation wall, the finished grade line in relation to the first-floor line should be determined. If the brickwork extends below grade, the concrete foundation wall should extend above grade, as shown in detail, to make the wall watertight. Assuming that this question is settled, draw the foundation wall and brick wall as shown.
4. Show floor joist set into pocket in brick wall and resting on foundation wall. The joists are set on ½″ mortar bed to assure a level floor.
5. *a.* Draw in rough floor, running it through to the brick wall.

b. Draw furring on inside of brick wall. The furring consists of 2″ x 3″ studs laid up flatwise to save space. The furring is necessary on the inside of a brick wall to provide an air space between the brick and the plaster. If it is omitted, moisture would penetrate through the wall into the plaster, resulting in an unhealthy condition. The furring strips are nailed into the brick joints and serve as nailing strips for lath or paneling.

c. Draw in the plaster line, and show grounds. The grounds act as a plaster stop and also as a nailing strip for the baseboard.

d. Finished floor can now be shown, running up to the baseboard.

e. Indicate materials by proper symbols and notes (see Fig. 44).

f. Dimensioning and lettering should be put in last.

LESSON 15

Sill Construction for Today's House

Today's house is a small house, small enough to fit comfortably on a city or suburban lot, small enough to be cared for easily by the maidless housewife, small enough to suit the average budget, which has to include the original cost, the carrying cost, and the cost of maintenance. Architects and builders face the challenge of inflated costs, material scarcities, and an unprecedented demand for housing caused by the war years of home-building inactivity. They are meeting that challenge by exploring the possibilities of new designs and new methods. Some of these will be studied in this lesson so that the student can draw plans for today's house. The sill sections (see Fig. 53) show three different types of construction.

A. Sill Section for Modern House for Outdoor Living

This type has no cellar, the floor being wood on concrete slab laid on gravel fill. Radiant heating (a system that is winning wide acclaim among architects and engineers) is supplied by hot-water pipes laid in the concrete floor.

Large Thermopane glass areas are used, opening out to a sheltered flagstone porch.

B. Sill Section for Concrete House Using Prefabricated Concrete Wall Panels

This system eliminates expensive wood forming, saves time by using a special vacuum-treated concrete, and produces an economical fire-resisting shell.

Concrete floor panels are made in precast sections and are finished with asphalt tile. The exterior wall panels are covered with a troweled surface of colored sand concrete while in the mold, no additional exterior treatment being required. Metallic insulation and plasterboard fixed to wood nailers, which are cast into the concrete panels, make up the interior.

C. Sill Section for an All-concrete House

Construction consists of 8″ cinder concrete blocks for exterior walls, with 4″ concrete floor on cinder fill. Note that the floor slab is insulated from direct exterior exposure.

The foundation wall extends down 4′-0″ to a concrete footing. This condition may vary according to the climate in which the house is to be built.

Interior walls are plastered on metal lath applied to metal furring channels.

Exterior walls can be protected by painting with two coats of Portland-cement paint.

PROBLEM

Sill sections. Copy Fig. 53, following the procedure shown in the progressive steps for drawing details of sill construction outlined in Lessons 12 to 14.

Figure 54 shows three additional types of construction.

SILL SECTIONS

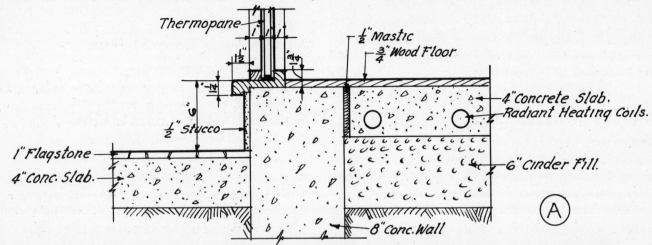

Thermopane

$\frac{1}{2}$" Mastic
$\frac{3}{4}$" Wood Floor

4" Concrete Slab.
Radiant Heating Coils.

$\frac{1}{2}$" stucco

1" Flagstone

4" Conc. Slab.

6" Cinder Fill.

8" Conc. Wall

· SILL SECTION FOR MODERN HOUSE FOR OUTDOOR LIVING ·

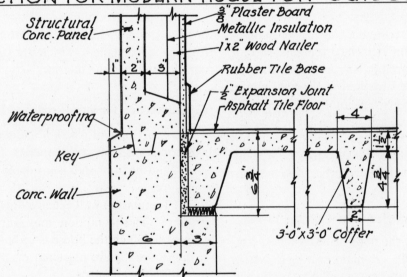

Structural Conc. Panel

$\frac{3}{8}$" Plaster Board
Metallic Insulation
1"x2" Wood Nailer

Rubber Tile Base

Waterproofing

$\frac{1}{2}$" Expansion Joint
Asphalt Tile Floor

Key

Conc. Wall

3'-0"x3'-0" Coffer

· SILL SECTION FOR HOUSE USING PREFABRICATED CONCRETE PANELS ·

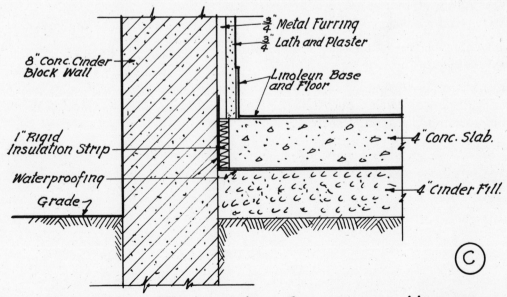

$\frac{3}{4}$" Metal Furring
$\frac{3}{4}$" Lath and Plaster

8" Conc. Cinder Block Wall

Linoleun Base and Floor

1" Rigid Insulation Strip

4" Conc. Slab.

Waterproofing

Grade

4" Cinder Fill.

· SILL SECTION FOR AN ALL CONCRETE HOUSE ·

Scale $1\frac{1}{2}$" = 1'-0"

FIGURE 53

55

D. Sill Section for Plywood House

This house is described in detail in Lesson 30. It has no cellar, the floors being linoleum on concrete slab. The foundation wall has a shelf to receive the floor slab and a curb to keep the wood sill aboveground for protection against dampness.

E. Sill Section for Low-cost Wood Construction

This is the type of streamlined wood-construction houses built in great numbers during the war and post-war critical periods, when restrictions and shortages made demands upon the skill, ingenuity, and sound construction experience of American builders.

There is no cellar. An air space of 2'-6" is allowed under the floor joist for circulation, pipes, wiring, etc.

This detail shows how available materials may be used to best advantage in platform-type sill construction.

F. Sill Section for Low-set-sill House

Special conditions requiring that the first floor be kept close to the outside grade, as in early colonial homes, which look best when set as close as possible to the ground, make it necessary to leave a shelf in the concrete wall to receive the floor joists.

PROBLEM

Sill sections. Copy Fig. 54, following the procedure shown in the progressive steps for drawing details of sill construction outlined in Lessons 12 to 14.

SILL SECTIONS

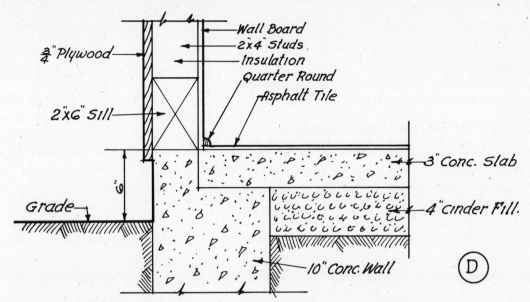

- Wall Board
- 2"x4" Studs
- Insulation
- Quarter Round
- Asphalt Tile
- ¾" Plywood
- 2"x6" Sill
- 3" Conc. Slab
- 4" Cinder Fill.
- Grade
- 10" Conc. Wall

Ⓓ

·SILL SECTION FOR PLYWOOD HOUSE·

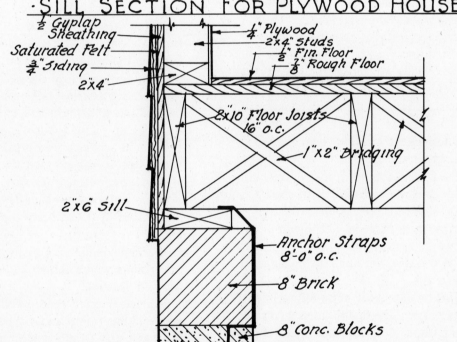

- ½" Guplap Sheathing
- ¼" Plywood
- 2"x4" Studs
- ½" Fin. Floor
- ⅞" Rough Floor
- Saturated Felt
- ¾" Siding
- 2"x4"
- 2"x10" Floor Joists 16" o.c.
- 1"x2" Bridging
- 2"x6" Sill
- Anchor Straps 8'-0" o.c.
- 8" Brick
- 8" Conc. Blocks

Ⓔ

·SILL SECTION FOR LOW-COST WOOD CONSTRUCTION·

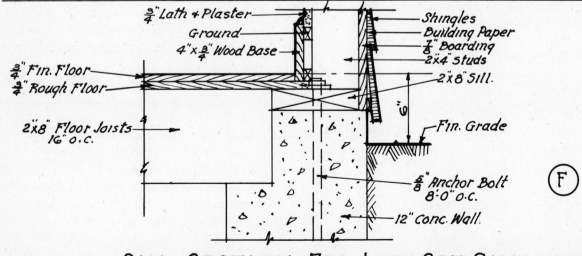

- ¾" Lath & Plaster
- Ground
- 4"x¾" Wood Base
- Shingles
- Building Paper
- ⅞" Boarding
- 2"x4" Studs
- ¾" Fin. Floor
- ⅞" Rough Floor
- 2"x8" Sill.
- 2"x8" Floor Joists 16" o.c.
- Fin. Grade
- ⅝" Anchor Bolt 8'-0" o.c.
- 12" Conc. Wall.

·SILL SECTION FOR LOW SET SILL·   Scale 1½"=1'-0"

FIGURE 54

57

LESSON 16

Progressive Steps for Drawing Double-hung Windows—Details

Windows are the eyes of a house. Not only have they the utilitarian purpose of admitting light and air to the interior and of permitting the inhabitants to view the outside world, but they also contribute greatly to the beauty or disfigurement of the completed house. Their number, placement, design, and proportions can make or mar the appearance of almost any house. Therefore, a thorough knowledge of their type, construction, and details is necessary to the good draftsman.

Double-hung wood windows are the most common type of window used in residential work. Usually a stock frame can be designated and can be obtained from the mill by catalogue number.

The architect will use stock sash and frame wherever possible because of the saving involved, but in special circumstances he will find it necessary to detail the window frames and have them made up at the mill.

In considering the window, the head section is taken through the top of the window, the jamb at the sides, and the sill at the bottom.

This problem is based on a double-hung window in a solid brick wall (see Fig. 55). The figure shows a complete construction detail and the progressive steps for drawing the head and sill sections. The draftsman should proceed with Steps 1, 2, 3, following these instructions to arrive at the finished detail. Draw only the finished project; do not draw Steps 1, 2, and 3 separately.

Use the following procedure to draw a double-hung-window detail in solid brick wall and also in brick-veneer and wood-frame construction.

In drawing any detail, first lay out lightly the entire detail. When this is completed, go over the lines with a clean, firm line.

PROBLEM

1. Use 12″ x 18″ sheet held vertically. Draw ½″ border and title box.
2. Draw section details at 3″ scale.

To Draw Head Section

1. *a.* Indicate the wall thickness, and show furring and plaster lines. Solid brick walls except in special cases are 4″, 8″, and 12″ thick, these being standard sizes for bricks. A solid brick wall should always be furred to allow an air space between the brick and plaster to prevent moisture getting through to the plaster.

2. *a.* Show 2″ setback in brick wall, back from the face of the wall the width of a brick (usually 3¾″ wide). The window box sets into this reveal and acts as a windbreak.

   Show steel angles as indicated. These angles are used to carry the brickwork over the window opening and are known as *lintels*. The size is determined by the width of the opening and the load it has to carry.

   b. Draw the main layout of the window box. Use dimensions where shown; otherwise, scale the finished drawing.

3. *a.* Next draw the staff bead, which covers the joint between the frame and the brick. This staff bead will vary from a small molding, as shown in this figure, to a complete architrave, according to the design of the building.

   b. Draw the plaster return, inside finish, and moldings, with the sash shown in the outside sash pocket. The dimension from the pulley stile to the glass is usually 2″. The thickness of the molding and the putty holding the glass in place is ⅜″ or ½″ (see full-size detail of sash, Fig. 57). The glass size is given on an elevation. Thus, $\frac{9}{11}$ means that the actual glass size is 9″ x 11″ and not the sight line.

   c. Show flashing at head section running through the wall over the steel lintels to protect them from moisture.

   d. Carry all wall, sash, frame, and trim lines down to the sill section. This practice will ensure

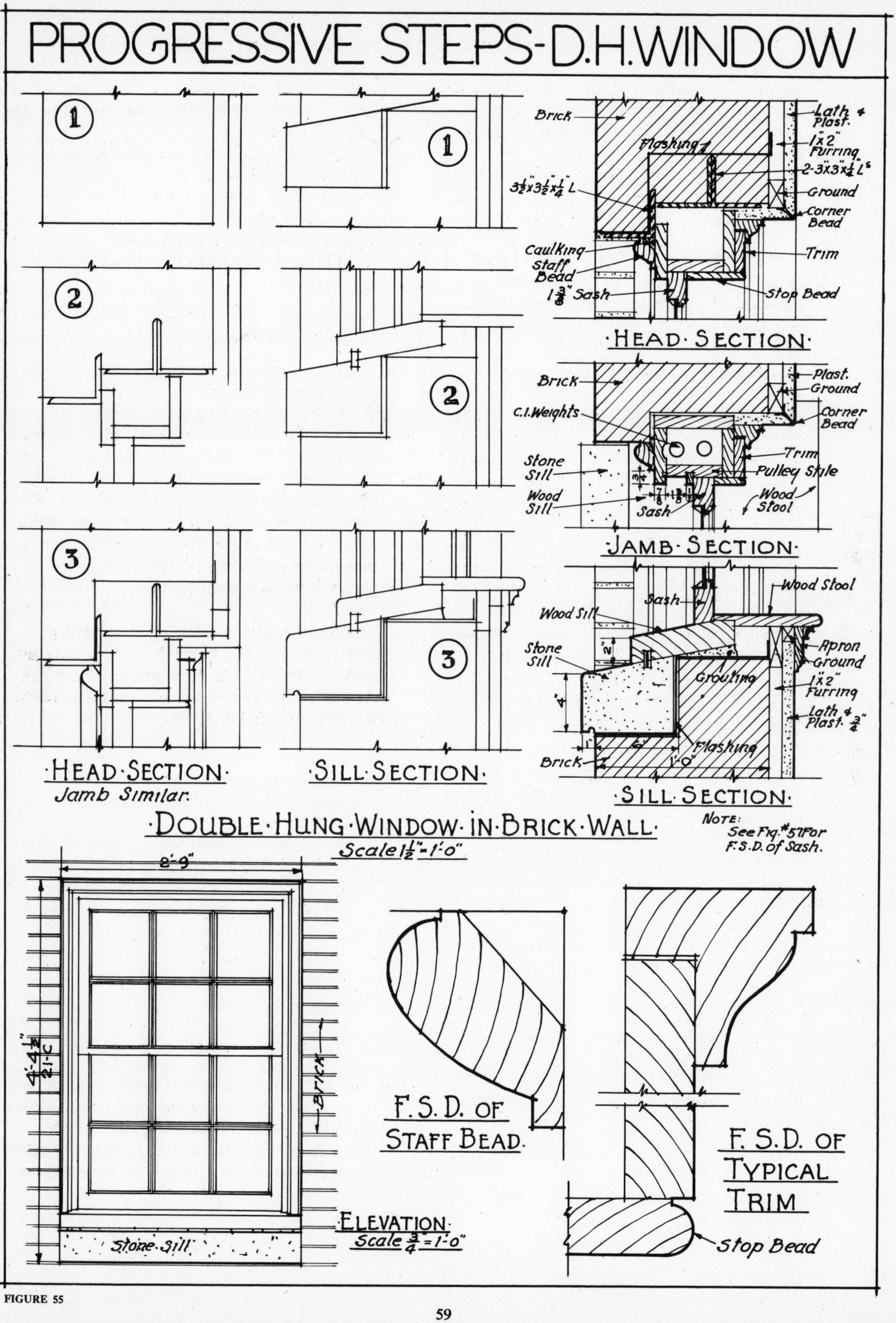

PROGRESSIVE STEPS-D.H.WINDOW

1

1

2

2

3

3

Brick — Lath & Plast.
Flashing — 1"x2" Furring
$3\frac{1}{2}"x3\frac{1}{2}"x\frac{1}{4}"L$ — 2-3"x3"x$\frac{1}{4}"L^s$
Ground
Corner Bead
Caulking
Staff Bead — Trim
$1\frac{3}{8}"$ Sash — Stop Bead

·HEAD·SECTION·

Brick — Plast. Ground
C.I.Weights — Corner Bead
Stone Sill — Trim
Pulley Stile
Wood Sill — Wood Stool
Sash

·JAMB·SECTION·

Wood Sill — Wood Stool
Sash
Stone Sill — Apron
Ground
1"x2" Furring
Grouting
Lath & Plast. $\frac{3}{4}"$
Brick — Flashing

·SILL·SECTION·

·HEAD·SECTION·
Jamb Similar.

·SILL·SECTION·

·DOUBLE·HUNG·WINDOW·IN·BRICK·WALL·
Scale $1\frac{1}{2}"=1'-0"$

NOTE:
See Fig.#57For
F.S.D. of Sash.

2'-9"

4'-4$\frac{3}{8}$"
2'-0"

Brick

Stone Sill

·ELEVATION·
Scale $\frac{3}{4}"=1'-0"$

F.S.D. of STAFF BEAD.

F.S.D. of TYPICAL TRIM

Stop Bead

FIGURE 55

59

that all construction and finish lines up and builds properly. Note that the jamb and sill sections are always drawn directly under the head section.

To draw the jamb section, follow the same procedure as in drawing the head section (see jamb section in finished detail, Fig. 55).

To Draw Sill Section

1. *a.* Draw in the masonry wall lines from the lines projected down from the members of the head and jamb sections. Leave the necessary setback to receive the stone sill.

   b. Carry down the furring and plaster lines.

   c. Insert stone-sill outline as shown, the slope of the sill being determined by the design of the window. Obviously, the sill must have enough pitch to ensure that the water flows off freely.

2. *a.* Next draw the wood sill. The thickness varies from $1\frac{3}{4}''$ to $2\frac{1}{4}''$, depending on the width of the sill. It should have pitch enough to make it watertight, and it should be wide enough to receive the staff bead, which has been projected down from the head section. The back of the sill is leveled off to receive the inside stool.

3. *a.* Draw the outline of the stool, and put in sash projected from above. The bottom rail of the sash is usually $2\frac{1}{2}''$ to the glass.

   b. Complete the window stool, showing ground for plaster stop and apron to cover the joint.

   c. Show slot in bottom of the wood sill and in the top of the stone sill, with shield inserted to act as a windbreak.

   d. Draw in grouting under wood sill to seal joint.

   e. Indicate flashing as shown with small groove on under side of stone sill for water drip.

Complete drawing by showing brick joints, and indicate proper material symbols (see Fig. 44).

Put in all notes and dimensions on head, jamb, and sill sections.

To Draw Elevation of Window

The height of a window in a brick wall must fit into an equal number of brick courses. Therefore before a window is drawn, the size of a brick and joint must be known. One brick and a joint make up a brick course. This usually runs $2\frac{3}{8}''$ or $2\frac{1}{2}''$. The width of the window can be any dimension desired. The size of the staff bead and sash must be determined. With all this information, proceed as follows, using $\frac{3}{4}''$ scale. Draw this elevation on the same sheet as the detail.

1. Draw brick opening first. Put in stone sill.
2. Show staff bead on jambs and head.
3. Draw in sash.
4. Show brick courses and dimensions as shown.
5. Draw full-size details to actual size, showing the profile of the moldings. The staff bead and typical trim shown here are used on the window details.
6. Put in all notes and dimensions.

LESSON 17

Double-hung Window in Brick-veneer and Wood-frame Wall

This detail (see Fig. 56) shows the complete working drawings for the construction of a double-hung window in a brick-veneer and a wood-frame wall. For actual construction purposes the architect would draw these details at full size, but in some cases, if dimensioned properly, it could be built from a 3″ scale detail.

BRICK-VENEER WALL

A brick-veneer house has the appearance of a solid brick house at a much lower construction cost. It is more expensive than the frame house but has the advantage of being more fireproof, having greater insulation value, and requiring smaller outlay for painting and upkeep.

The wood frame is always built first, the single layer of brick being applied afterward as a veneer. There should be 6″ from the outside face of brick to the wood frame to allow ample air space. This space not only allows the drying out of any moisture that comes through the brickwork but also provides good insulation. The brick is bonded with corrugated metal clips set into joints at intervals and nailed to the boarding. A steel angle lintel is used at the head to carry the brick, above. Flashing is carried over the lintel, bent back, and nailed to the boarding. The building paper, which is applied to the entire boarding, is run down over the flashing to make the house watertight.

The window box is secured to the wood construction, the frame running in beyond the face of the brick to allow calking space before the staff bead is applied. This acts as a good windbreak. Flashing is carried under brick sill and nailed to boarding.

PROBLEMS

Double-hung Window in Brick-veneer Wall

1. Use 12″ x 18″ sheet. Draw ½″ border and title box.

2. Draw window in brick-veneer wall, frame wall, and mullion section at 3″ scale.
3. Draw elevation of window at ¾″ scale.
4. When completed, erase all unnecessary lines, and clean up sheet.
5. Follow the procedure described for window in solid brick wall (page 58). Measure with scale where dimensions are not given.

Method of Procedure

1. Start with head section first, using light line.
2. Draw wood frame with boarding and plaster.
3. For figures not shown on head section, see jamb and sill sections.
4. Show brick veneer with steel lintel and flashing.
5. Draw window frame and sash as shown.
6. Apply staff bead and interior trim (see Figs. 55 and 57 for full-size details).
7. Project all construction and finish lines down so that jamb and sill sections will line up directly under.
8. Do not dimension, apply notes, or show material symbols until entire detail is blocked out.
9. Draw jamb section similar to head section, making sure all parts line up.
10. Project lines down, and draw sill section as shown.
11. Draw wood frame first with sill, stool, apron, and sash. Slope of sill should pitch enough to ensure watertightness.
12. Draw brick veneer and brick sill following slope of wood sill. Show flashing under sill.
13. When entire detail is blocked out, go over with a firm line, show material symbols, and put on all notes and dimensions.
14. Outline profile with a heavy line.

Double-hung Window in Wood-frame Wall

In most cases, stock frames are used for windows in wood-frame construction. The most common are known as the *Boston style* and the *Western style*, the difference in these types being the extra piece on the frame for installing screen or storm sash. This detail shows the meeting rail and muntin section, which is typical for all sash. See elevation for location.

Method of Procedure

1. Draw head section first, starting with rough studs and applying boarding, frame, plaster, and inside and outside finish. Follow procedure similar to that shown in Fig. 55.

2. Project all members from head section down in order to line up jamb section.
3. Draw jamb, using same procedure.
4. Project lines down to draw meeting rail and muntins.
5. Project down, and draw sill as shown.
6. Refer to isometric drawing for help to visualize a section. It is not necessary to draw this.
7. Draw mullion next, similar to jamb section. The mullion is the dividing member between two windows. It houses the weights in a double-hung window.
8. Add all notes and dimensions, and show material symbols.
9. Go over with a firm line, and outline profile.

WOOD DOUBLE-HUNG WINDOWS

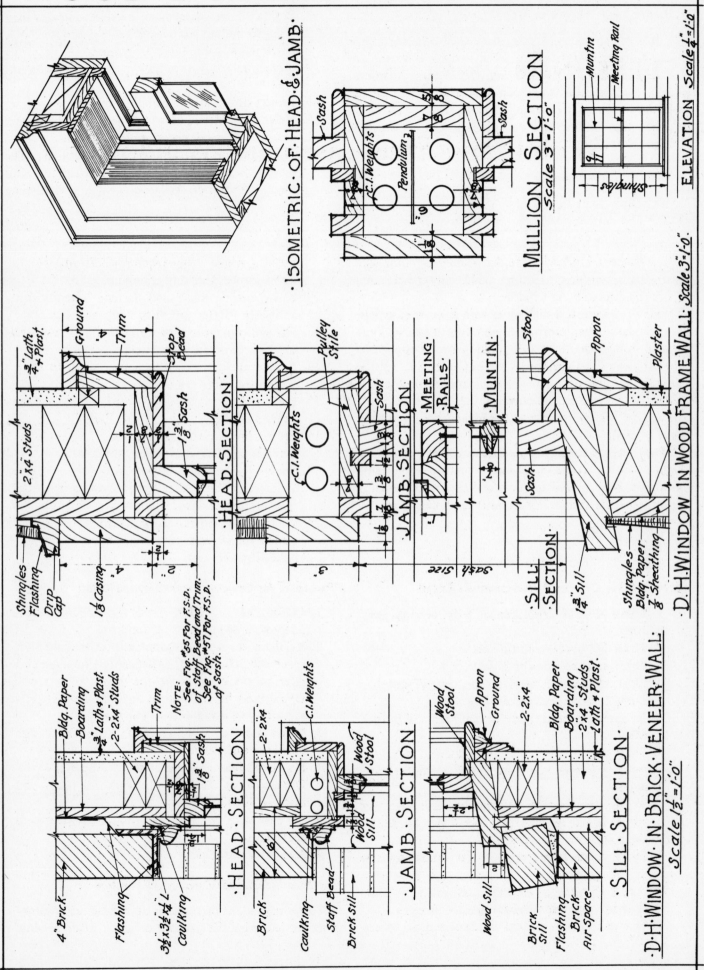

ISOMETRIC OF HEAD & JAMB.

MULLION SECTION. Scale 3"=1'-0"

ELEVATION Scale ¼"=1'-0"

Muntin

Meeting Rail

Shingles

Sash

C.I. Weights

Pendulum

Sash

HEAD SECTION.

JAMB SECTION.

SILL SECTION.

D.H. WINDOW IN WOOD FRAME WALL. Scale 3"=1'-0"

¾" Lath & Plast.

Ground

Trim

Stop Bead

1⅜" Sash

2"x4" Studs

Shingles

Flashing

Drip Cap

1⅜" Casing

Pulley Stile

C.I. Weights

Sash

MEETING RAILS.

MUNTIN.

Stool

Apron

Plaster

Sash

1¾" Sill

Shingles

Bldg. Paper

⅞" Sheathing

NOTE: See Fig. #55 For F.S.D. of Staff Bead and Trim. See Fig. #57 For F.S.D. of Sash.

Bldg. Paper

Boarding

¾" Lath & Plast.

2-2"x4" Studs

Trim

1⅜" Sash

4" Brick

Flashing

3½"x3½"x¼" L

Caulking

HEAD SECTION.

D.H. WINDOW IN BRICK VENEER WALL. Scale 1½"=1'-0"

2-2"x4

C.I. Weights

Wood Stool

Wood Sill

Brick

Caulking

Staff Bead

Brick Sill

JAMB SECTION.

Wood Stool

Apron

Ground

2-2"x4

Bldg. Paper

Boarding

2"x4 Studs

Lath & Plast.

Wood Sill

Brick Sill

Flashing

Brick

Air Space

SILL SECTION.

FIGURE 56

63

LESSON 18

Wood- and Steel-casement Windows

A casement window is one that is hinged on the side swinging in or out. It requires a different type of frame from the double-hung window.

One of the greatest difficulties with a wood casement is to make it weatherproof, especially if it swings in as shown in this detail. A drip mold is always applied to the bottom rail to keep the water out at the sill. If the sash swings inward, a screen can be applied on the outside. If the sash swings outward, then the screen must be inside, and ordinarily either a hinged or a roll-up type is used.

The steel casement set in mastic cement ensures a tight window. It can be set directly on the wood frame as shown here or in a special wood surround, which is applied to the frame. Steel casements nearly always swing outward.

PROBLEM (see Fig. 57)

Procedure for Drawing Wood-casement Detail

1. Use a 12″ x 18″ sheet, planning use of space carefully.
2. Draw ½″ border and title box.
3. Draw scale sections at 3″ scale.
4. Draw elevation of steel casement at ¾″ scale.
5. Draw full-size sections as shown.
6. Be sure that head, jamb, and sill align with each other.
7. Draw head section first very lightly, following same principle used in drawing double-hung window.
8. Try to visualize the way in which the casement would be constructed, and follow step by step as the contractor would build it.
9. Draw rough frame first, 2″ x 4″ studs (actually 1¾″ x 3¾″).
10. Apply boarding, ground, and plaster. Scale drawing where dimensions are not given.
11. Frame for sash should be drawn next. Keep finished frame away from rough frame ½″ to allow for wedging and truing up.
12. Show outside finish and flashing, interior trim and sash. Refer to full-size detail of sash.
13. Do not dimension or show material symbols until whole detail is complete.
14. Project all lines down to jamb section to make sure everything lines up.
15. Follow the procedure for drawing jamb section as used for head.
16. Project lines down to sill section.
17. Draw rough frame, boarding, and plaster.
18. Show sill, stool, apron, and sash.
19. Complete whole detail by showing material symbols, dimensions, and notes.
20. Go over entire detail with a clean, firm line, and outline profile as shown with a heavy line.
21. Add titles and scale.

Procedure for Drawing Steel-casement Detail

1. Follow the procedure used for wood-casement window, drawing head section first.
2. As there are several manufacturers making steel casements, check with specifications for type and refer to stock catalogue for details of sections. Detail used here is typical but may vary slightly according to manufacturer's specialty.
3. When drawing 3″ scale detail, refer to full-size detail for sash sections.
4. Project all lines down to align sill properly.
5. Dimension as shown, and apply all notes and material symbols.
6. Go over with firm line, and outline profile with a heavy line.
7. Add titles and scale.

To Draw Small-scale Elevation of Window

The windows are first drawn on the ¼″ scale elevations to determine the size and design. Each window

64

CASEMENT-WINDOW DETAILS

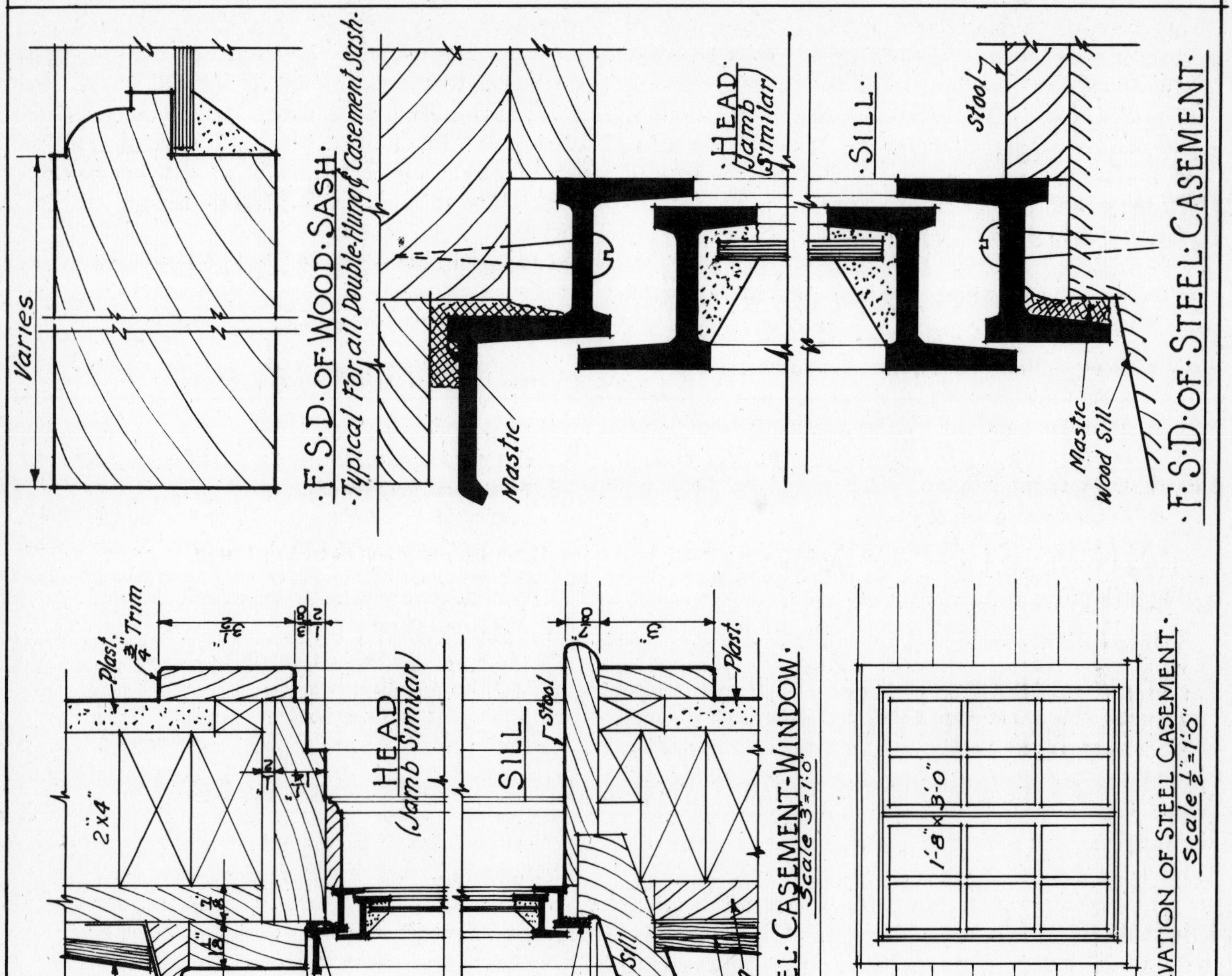

Varies

·F·S·D·OF·WOOD·SASH·

·Typical·For all·Double-Hung·Casement·Sash·

Mastic

HEAD (Jamb Similar)

SILL

Stool

Mastic
Wood Sill

·F·S·D·OF·STEEL·CASEMENT·

Plast.
¾"Trim
3½"
½"

2"x 4"

HEAD (Jamb Similar)

SILL
Stool

Plast.
3"
½"

Shingles
Flashing
Mastic

Mastic
Window Size

Shingles
Boarding
Sill

·STEEL·CASEMENT-WINDOW·
Scale 3"=1'-0"

1'-8"x 3'-0"

Shingles

·ELEVATION·OF·STEEL·CASEMENT·
Scale ½"=1'-0"

¾"Lath & Plast.
⅝" Trim
3½"
1½"
2"

2"x 4"

·HEAD·
Sash
7"
8"

Shingles
Flashing
Drip Cap
Casing

Plast.
Ground
Wood Stool
Sash

·JAMB·
Wood Sill
3½"

Boarding
Shingles

Stool
Apron
Plast.

Sash
Drip Mold
Sill 1"-2¼"
2"x 4"

·SILL·

Shingles
⅞"Boarding

·WOOD·CASEMENT·
Scale 3"=1'-0"

FIGURE 57

65

not of stock design is then drawn at larger scale to give the contractor a clear picture. It is generally drawn on the same sheet with the detailed sections. The elevation shows the over-all size of the window, the number of lights, and the trim. The elevation alone is of no value to the contractor; it must be accompanied by the section to show the construction behind the surface and the profile of the moldings.

Procedure for Drawing Elevation of Steel-casement Window

1. Draw outline of sash, from dimensions given, with a light line.
2. Show trim and sill. Refer to 3″ scale sections for size.
3. Draw in muntins.
4. Go over with a firm line.

An elevation of a wood casement would be drawn in the same way.

Full-size Details

The drawings shown at full-size detail give a true picture of the wood and steel sashes as they actually are. It is necessary to make a full-size section of all special woodwork so that the mill can grind the cutting knives to make the moldings. It is not necessary to detail stock sash, trim, or moldings; for the mill makes these up in large quantities, and they can be ordered from catalogues. The full-size wood-sash detail shown here can be used as a typical detail for all sash shown in this book. The thickness and width of the rail will vary slightly.

The full-size detail of the steel sash shows how the steel window frame is fastened to the wood frame and how the steel sash operates.

To Draw Full-size Details of Wood Sash

1. Outline lightly first.
2. Go over with firm line.
3. Show material symbols.

To Draw Full-size Detail of Steel Sash

1. Outline lightly wood frame as shown.
2. Apply steel frame.
3. Draw in steel sash as shown.
4. Outline with firm line.
5. Show material symbols and notes.
6. Put in titles.

LESSON 19

Exterior Door in Wood-frame Construction

This lesson introduces the student to the subject of doors. The exterior door of any building is very important. Almost always, the first impression made upon an observer is that created by the entrance or doorway, for this is the first unit that emerges from the general appearance of the façade. The harmony of the doorway with the complete structure should suggest a cordial welcome to enter and enjoy the hospitality of the house. Guests as well as owner should enjoy the beauty of a doorway. Many an otherwise beautiful house is marred by a poorly designed or executed doorway.

It is advisable, therefore, to study the many charming doorways that can be found in almost every locality. Make sketches of them in your notebook. Draw the more interesting details. Examine them closely if you can to find out how you would treat them if you were asked to make construction drawings of them.

This and the following lessons on doors will teach you how to proceed.

The door detail shown in Fig. 58 is an actual working drawing used in the construction of the main entrance for the Marshfield house plans shown in Fig. 80. The architect would probably detail the sections at full scale to show the profile of the moldings, etc.; but, if dimensioned thoroughly, it could be built from this 3″ scale drawing. The elevation shows how the interior and exterior are handled by showing half of each, dividing the elevation with a center line. The ¾″ scale is the most commonly used for this part of the detail. This is a very usual procedure where the door is symmetrical; for it saves time in drafting, and all the necessary information can be shown on half the elevation. However, the full elevation should be studied both inside and out in sketch form to determine the proper design and scale.

The method of using section reference lines is employed here to designate the area from which the section is taken. This means that the 3″ scale section A-A may be described as a cut through the head of the transom on the line A-A showing the construction behind the finished surface. The same holds true for sections B-B, C-C, and D-D. This method is simple and clear.

The exterior elevation shows a true picture of the outside of the doorway in relation to the rest of the building including the door, the fluted pilaster, trim, cornice, step, and shingles.

The interior elevation shows the ceiling in relation to the transom and also the design of the trim to meet a special condition at the head. Note that the flat part of the trim is narrower at the head than it is on the sides (jamb). This is because of the distance left between the transom and the ceiling. The 3″ scale section shows this in detail. The interior also shows the wall treatment, cornice, baseboard, and distance from floor to ceiling. The architect would study the main entrance first on the ¼″ scale elevation. When the proper design and scale were settled, he would then draw it at ¾″ scale as shown here.

PROBLEM

Procedure for Drawing Elevation of Door Detail (see Fig. 58)

1. Use 12″ x 18″ sheet, planning carefully. Do not crowd elevation and section too closely together.
2. Draw ½″ border and title box.
3. Use ¾″ scale, and check all reference notes.
4. Draw outline of door first from dimensions given.
5. Refer to detailed section for dimensions not shown on elevation.
6. Draw center line through middle of door.
7. Show transom above door.
8. Show floor and grade line.
9. Draw in cornice lines.
10. Draw outside lines of pilaster. Complete by adding necking mold, cap, and base molds.
11. Show wood sill and concrete step with flagstone.
12. Complete exterior by showing trim and shingles.
13. Show panels in door.

14. Draw in floor and ceiling lines.
15. Complete interior elevation by showing trim, cornice, base, and wall finish.
16. Outline with a firm line, and erase all lines not needed.
17. Apply all notes and dimensions as shown.
18. Add titles, scale, section lines, and letters.

To Draw 3″ Scale Sections

1. Start with head section *A-A*, showing rough frame first, 2″ x 4″ (actually 1¾″ x 3¾″). Draw very lightly.
2. Show boarding and ¾″ piece on inside.
3. Apply finished frame, leaving space for wedging to true up frame.
4. Show exterior trim with start of roof cornice.
5. Sash, interior trim, and plaster ceiling shown next.
6. Project all lines down so that detail will align.
7. Do not dimension or show material symbols until entire detail is complete.
8. Using lines projected down from above, draw transom section *B-B*.
9. Project lines down again, drawing jamb section *C-C*, using same procedure as used for drawing head section *A-A*.
10. Use dimensions where shown, and scale if no dimensions are shown.
11. Project lines down, and draw sill section *D-D* in the manner described above.
12. Dimension as shown, and show material symbols and notes.
13. Go over with a clean, firm line, and outline profile with a heavy line as shown.
14. Put on section reference letters, title, and scale.

DOOR DETAIL IN WOOD WALL

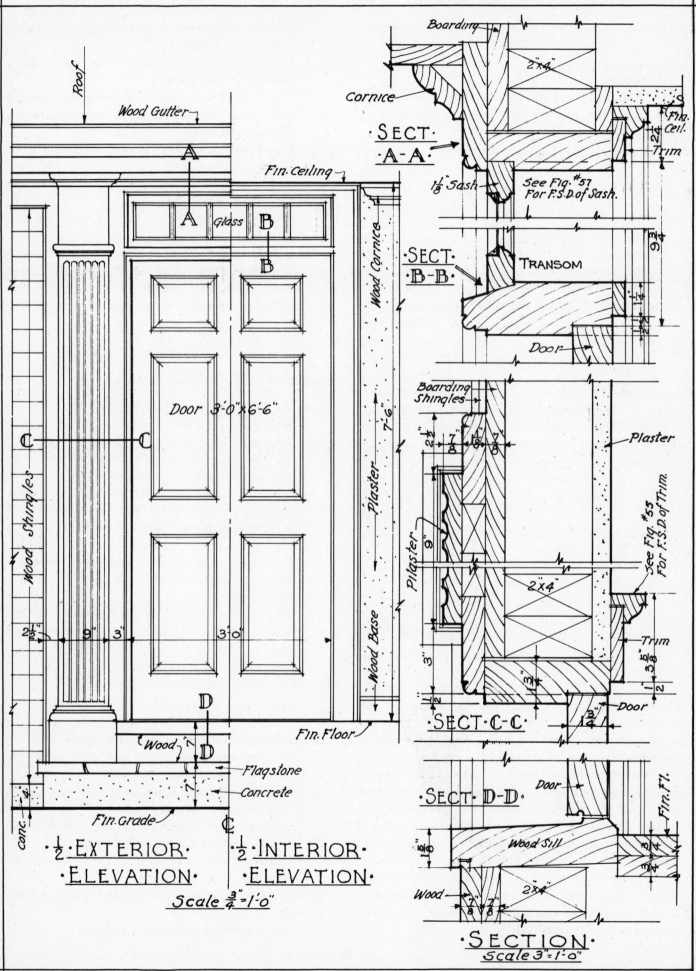

Roof

Wood Gutter

A

Fin. Ceiling

A Glass B

B

B

Door 3'-0"x6'-6"

C C C

Wood Shingles

2½" 9" 3' 3'-0"

Wood Cornice

Plaster 7'-6"

Wood Base

Fin. Floor

D D

Wood 7"

Flagstone

7" Concrete

Fin. Grade

conc. 4"

C

·½ EXTERIOR· ·ELEVATION·

·½ INTERIOR· ·ELEVATION·

Scale ¾"=1'-0"

Boarding

2"x4"

Cornice

SECT· A-A

Fin. Ceil.

2¼

Trim

1⅛ Sash

See Fig. #57 For F.S.D. of Sash.

9¾

SECT· B-B

TRANSOM

Door

1¼

2⅜

Boarding Shingles

2½ 7 1⅛ 7 ⅞ ⅞ ⅞

Plaster

Plaster 9"

See Fig. #55 For F.S.D. of Trim.

2"x4"

Trim

3

3⅝

m 1½

SECT· C-C

Door

3 14

SECT· D-D

Door

Fin. Fl.

Wood Sill

1⅝⅛

Wood 7 7 ⅞ ⅞

2"x4"

·SECTION· Scale 3"=1'-0"

FIGURE 58

69

LESSON 20

Exterior Door in Brick Wall

This drawing (see Fig. 59) is a 3″ scale copy of a full-size detail for the construction of an exterior door in a brick-veneer house. It is set up here exactly as the architect would present the detail to the contractor. The ¾″ scale elevation shows a picture of the door as seen from the outside, including the brickwork around it. It shows the type of door and transom with all the necessary dimensions for the mill. As explained in previous lessons, this doorway, being in a brick wall, must be dimensioned to fit into the required brick coursing from bottom to top. The figure 8′-6½″ with the indication 41-C directly under it tells the contractor that, within the figure 8′-6½″, there are exactly 41 bricks and 41 joints using a 2½″ brick coursing. A brick course equals one brick and one joint. The brick arch at the head shows the style and pattern required. All bricks in this arch must radiate from the point indicated.

The sectional detail shows the construction hidden behind the surface that is shown in the elevation. It shows the width and thickness of the various parts, and the elevation shows the length. The sectional detail also gives the mill the information needed to mill out the frame and trim. It shows the profile of all moldings, and from this profile the mill grinds the knives to make the moldings. The detail shows also the steel angle, known as the *lintel*, holding the brickwork over the head of the door, with the flashing running over the angle to protect it from moisture. The top member of the outside trim is nailed into place after the calking has been packed in to make the frame weather-tight. The blocking shown indicates only that the space must be blocked out to receive the finished frame and trim.

Note that the trim on the transom-bar section has a bead, which will miter with the bead on the main architrave.

The slope of the wood sill must be sufficient to shed water. The groove in the bottom of the door acts as a drip for any water that might roll under. Note the flashing under the wood sill.

The outside face of the brick should be 6″ out from the face of the studs. This allows sufficient space between the boarding and the brickwork for any mortar that may bulge through. It also allows an air space, which is good insulation.

PROBLEM

Procedure for Drawing Door Detail

1. Use 12″ x 18″ sheet, planning carefully for two elevations and section.
2. Draw in ½″ border line and title box.
3. Draw exterior and interior elevation of door at ¾″ scale; assume ceiling height is 8′-6″.
4. Copy 3″ scale section as shown.
5. Draw ¾″ scale elevation first, using dimensions shown and sectional detail for reference.
6. Draw over-all brick opening first.
7. Show trim around opening, and put in wood sill.
8. Draw in transom bar and sash.
9. Show door panels.
10. Indicate brickwork each side of door, using 2½″ brick coursing. One brick + one joint = 2½″, brick = 2″.
11. Show brick arch as indicated.
12. Put on all dimensions and notes.

Sectional Drawing

1. As the wood-frame construction would be built first, start with head section and draw the rough 2″ x 4″ frame, boarding, and plaster.
2. Show brickwork and lintel.
3. Put in finished frame, sash, and trim.
4. Project all points down to ensure work aligning properly, and draw transom-bar section.
5. Projecting lines down again, draw sill section as shown, the wood frame first.
6. Put on all dimensions, notes, and material symbols.
7. Go over profile with a firm, clean line.

EXTERIOR DOOR IN BRICK WALL

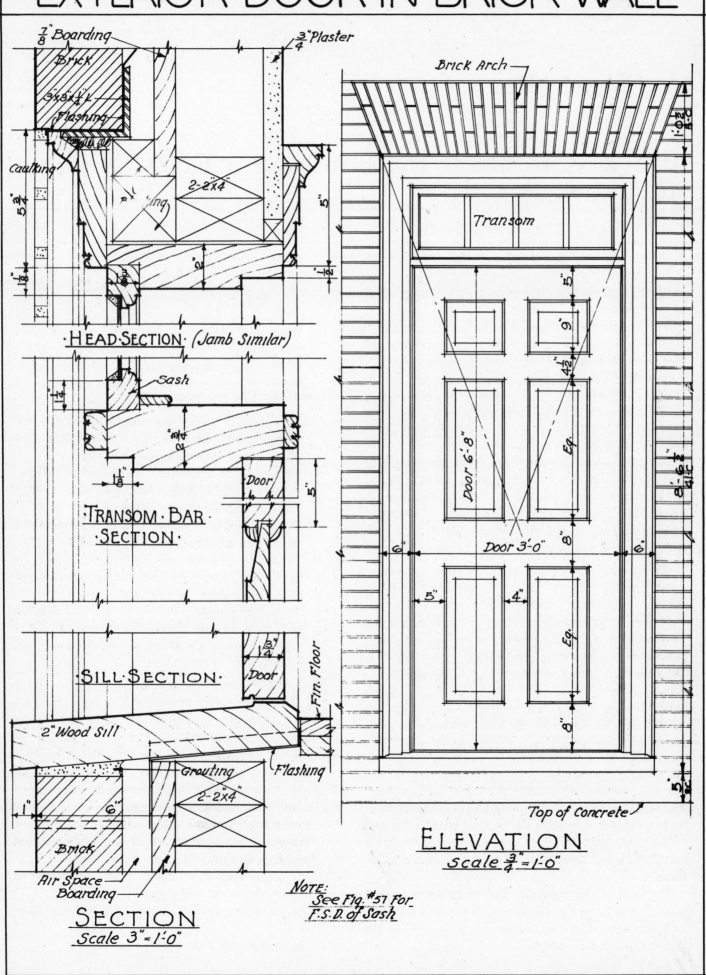

$\frac{7}{8}$"Boarding

Brick

$\frac{3}{4}$"Plaster

$3\times3\times\frac{1}{4}$"L

Flashing

Caulking

$5\frac{3}{4}$"

$1\frac{1}{8}$"

2-2"x4"

5"

2"

$1\frac{1}{2}$"

·HEAD·SECTION· (Jamb Similar)

$1\frac{1}{4}$"

Sash

$1\frac{1}{8}$"

$\frac{1}{2}$"

Door

5"

·TRANSOM·BAR·
SECTION·

$\frac{3}{4}$"

Door

·Fin. Floor·

·SILL·SECTION·

2" Wood Sill

Grouting

Flashing

2-2"x4"

1"

6"

Brick

Air Space

Boarding

SECTION
Scale 3"=1'-0"

NOTE:
See Fig. #57 For
F.S.D. of Sash

Brick Arch

Transom

Door 6'-8"

Door 3'-0"

5"

9"

$4\frac{1}{2}$"

Eq.

8"

6"

5"

4"

Eq.

8"

6"

Eq.

Top of Concrete

ELEVATION
Scale $\frac{3}{4}$"=1'-0"

FIGURE 59

71

LESSON 21

Progressive Steps for Drawing a Cornice Detail

Before starting to draw a cornice detail, all the necessary information should be obtained from the small-scale drawings and the specifications.

For these practice sheets it is to be assumed that the design of the cornice, the roof pitch, type of gutter, and plate height, along with the material to be used, have been settled and that we are about to proceed with the drawing. There are many types of cornice details, determined by the type and design of the building. However, the method used here can be applied to any type of cornice.

Where a masonry wall is used, proceed in the same manner, starting with the masonry wall and plate instead of the wood-stud wall. Draw all framing lumber actual size after being planed down. Thus, a 2″ x 8″ rafter would be 1¾″ x 7¾″ when delivered to the job.

Refer to millwork catalogues for finish sizes, for wood gutters, molding, etc. (see the molding sheet, Fig. 41, for profiles of moldings to make up a cornice).

If the draftsman keeps in mind at all times how the contractor would build the cornice and tries to follow this procedure step by step in his drawing, he will be able to visualize and understand the detail more clearly. A student should not proceed with any of these details unless he understands what he is drawing. He can make sure that he understands by referring to other details and scale drawings and checking all notes.

PROBLEM

Procedure for Drawing Cornice Detail (see Fig. 60)

1. Use 9″ x 12″ sheet.
2. Draw ½″ border and title box.

3. Draw only Step 4, following procedure outlined in Steps 1, 2, and 3 shown in Fig. 60.
4. Draw 2″ x 4″ wall studs with plate. The plate usually consists of two 2″ x 4″ studs nailed together and halved at the corners of the building.
5. Draw rafter with correct roof pitch determined by elevation, and locate floor joists. Indicate the lines of roof boarding and roof material, each ⅞″ thick and drawn to the extreme projection of cornice. This is determined by scaling the ¼″ scale elevations. For this drawing, measurements can be taken from the finished detail shown in Step 4.
6. Draw top and bottom line of finished cornice as scaled and dimensioned from detail shown in Step 4. This would ordinarily be taken from the ¼″ scale drawings. Draw in profile of cornice mold. (In this case the wood gutter forms the top member of the cornice.) Draw in gutter as shown, with fascia board and soffit of cornice.
7. Show outside boarding and siding. Complete cornice by adding bed mold. Indicate roof material; show strapping on ceiling and lath and plaster on walls and ceiling.

This cornice detail is a very simple one for a small wood-frame house with the gutter forming part of the cornice. The same procedure should be followed in drawing any type of cornice, whether it be for a wood or a masonry building.

In detailing, the specifications and the small scale drawings must be followed specifically; for the contractor figures the job from the ¼″ scale drawings and specifications, and any change in the details may call for an extra charge to the owner, which should be avoided as much as possible.

PROGRESSIVE STEPS - CORNICE

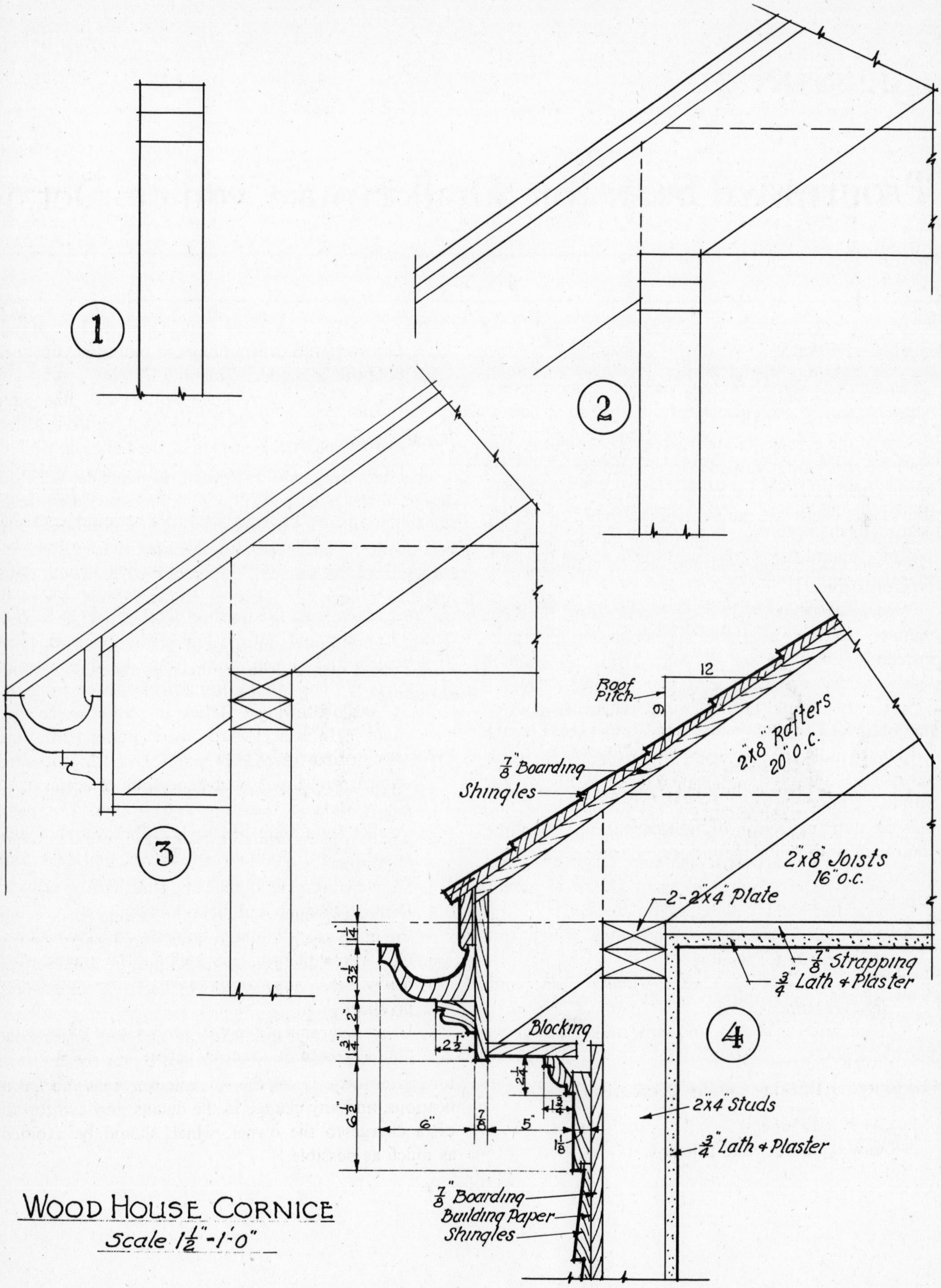

① ② ③ ④

Roof Pitch — 12 / 9

2"x8" Rafters 20" o.c.

⅞" Boarding
Shingles

2"x8" Joists 16" o.c.

2-2"x4" Plate

⅞" Strapping
¾" Lath & Plaster

Blocking

2"x4" Studs

¾" Lath & Plaster

⅞" Boarding
Building Paper
Shingles

WOOD HOUSE CORNICE
Scale 1½"-1'0"

FIGURE 60

73

LESSON 22

Cornice Detail for Small House and Porch

Small-house Cornice

The detail in Fig. 61 shows a simple and inexpensive method of constructing a cornice for a small stock house. It is made up with a stock wood gutter applied to the boarding, with a stock bed mold on the underside to cover the joint between the fascia board and the gutter. The width of the fascia board varies according to the location of the window. Building paper should be laid carefully behind the gutter and turned up on the roof boarding to prevent leaks.

The roof pitch is shown as a 12″ run and a 10″ rise. Note the strapping on the underside of the floor joists to true up the ceiling.

PROBLEM

Procedure for Drawing Small-house Cornice (see Fig. 61)

1. Use 12″ x 18″ sheet, planning carefully.
2. Draw ½″ border line and title box.
3. Follow steps shown in Fig. 60.
4. Lay out lightly first.
5. Show rough construction first, 2″ x 4″ studs, plate, rafters, and floor joist. (Draw to actual size after planing about ⅛″ on all sides.)
6. Apply roof boarding, wall boarding, gutter, and outside trim for window.
7. Draw in strapping, plaster, window frame, and interior trim.
8. Dimension as shown, and show material symbols and notes.

9. Go over with a firm line, and outline profile.
10. Add title and scale.

Porch Gutter

This detail is made up special, to coincide with the design of the house. It is a 3″ scale copy taken from the actual full-size working drawing of a porch that has been built. The copper hung gutter is used here to form part of the cornice. The roof is covered with slate and has a very flat pitch, as shown by the diagram. Lead-coated copper flashing is used to ensure water-tightness. The plate consists of a 4″ x 6″ beam held up by wood posts. The ceiling consists of ¾″ wood sheathing.

Procedure for Drawing Porch Cornice

1. Draw plate first with rafter as shown, using light line.
2. Apply roof boarding, fascia on ends of rafters and moldings.
3. Show casing around plate and sheathing on ceiling.
4. Draw in flashing and metal hung gutter.
5. Put in all notes, material symbols, and dimensions.
6. Go over with firm line, and outline profile with heavy line. Erase all unnecessary lines, and clean up sheet.
7. Draw diagrams of types of roofs shown so as to be able to recognize them by name.

SMALL HOUSE & PORCH CORNICE

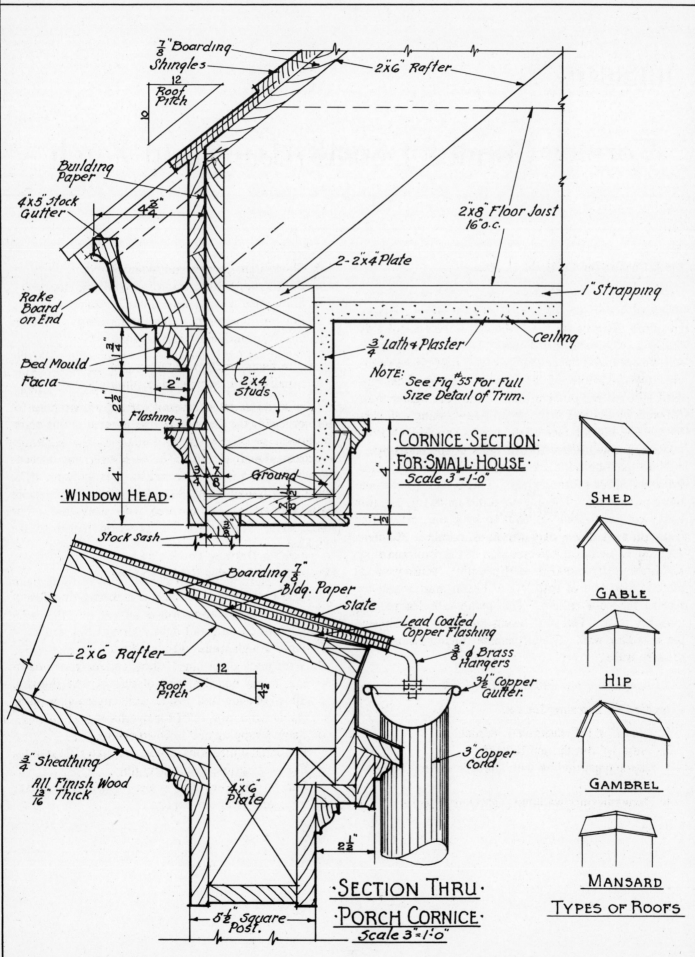

$\frac{7}{8}$" Boarding

Shingles

12
Roof Pitch

2"x6" Rafter

Building Paper

4"x5" Stock Gutter

$\frac{3}{4}$"

2"x8" Floor Joist 16" o.c.

Rake Board on End

2-2"x4" Plate

1" Strapping

Bed Mould

$\frac{3}{4}$" Lath & Plaster

Ceiling

Facia

2"x4" Studs

NOTE: See Fig #55 For Full Size Detail of Trim.

Flashing

4"

2"

$\frac{3}{4}$" $\frac{7}{8}$"

Ground

·CORNICE·SECTION· ·FOR·SMALL·HOUSE·
Scale 3"=1'-0"

4"

WINDOW HEAD·

Stock Sash

SHED

GABLE

Boarding $\frac{7}{8}$"

Bldg. Paper

Slate

Lead Coated Copper Flashing

2"x6" Rafter

Roof Pitch

12

$4\frac{1}{2}$

$\frac{3}{8}$" d Brass Hangers

$3\frac{1}{2}$" Copper Gutter.

HIP

$\frac{3}{4}$" Sheathing

All Finish Wood $\frac{13}{16}$" Thick

4"x6" Plate

3" Copper Cond.

GAMBREL

$2\frac{1}{2}$"

·SECTION THRU· ·PORCH CORNICE·
Scale 3"=1'-0"

$5\frac{1}{2}$" square Post.

MANSARD

TYPES OF ROOFS

FIGURE 61

75

LESSON 23

Cornice Details *(Continued)*

Brick Cornice for Cinder-block House

The detail in Fig. 62 shows the use of bricks in constructing a cornice for a cinder-block house. Bricks are more appropriate than wood in this case, for this house is an all-masonry house. The walls and floors are masonry, and the ceiling joists are steel beams spanning the full width of the house. Cinder blocks are used here for the outside walls. They are lighter than concrete blocks and make up a better-looking wall surface. The outside face of the blocks should be waterproofed and painted with two coats of special paint.

Note that the middle row of bricks has every other brick set back to form dentils. This makes the cornice more interesting. There is no gutter on this house, for heavy copper flashing extends to keep the roof water from running down over the brick cornice. Cement grouting is used at the intersection of the roof boarding and brickwork to make it weather-tight. A heavy wood plate is made up of two 2" x 6" beams and is used to receive the roof rafters. This plate is bolted to the masonry wall. The steel beams have a 4" bearing on the masonry wall. Metal channel furring is used on the side walls.

PROBLEM

Procedure for Drawing Cornice

1. Use 12" x 18" sheet, held vertical.
2. Draw ½" border and title box.
3. Divide paper in half with line, and use top half for this detail.
4. Draw masonry wall first, lightly at 3" scale.

5. Show brick cornice and wood plate.
6. Put in roof rafters, boarding, and shingles.
7. Show steel beams, ceiling, and wall finish.
8. Put on dimensions, notes, and material symbols.
9. Go over outline with a firm line.

Roof Overhang for Plywood House (Cornice) (see Fig. 73 for small-scale drawings of this house)

This is the architect's detail for the construction of the cornice for the plywood house featured in this book. It shows a simple, inexpensive method of constructing a wide overhanging roof. This wide overhang protects the side wall of the house from both rain and sun. The outside walls consist of ¾" plywood, and the inside walls and ceiling are covered with wallboard. The soffit of the overhang is ⅝" plywood nailed to the blocking.

Procedure for Drawing Roof Overhang

1. Use bottom half of sheet containing drawing of cinder-block-house cornice.
2. Lay out entire detail lightly, first at 1½" scale.
3. Draw rough studs and plate first.
4. With pitch determined, show rafters, roof boarding, fascia board at end of rafters, and shingles.
5. Show outside and inside wall covering, window frame, trim, and soffit for overhang.
6. Show strapping and finished ceiling.
7. Put on all dimensions, notes, and material symbols.
8. Go over outline with a firm line.
9. Put on all titles and scale. Erase unnecessary lines, and clean up paper.

CORNICE DETAILS

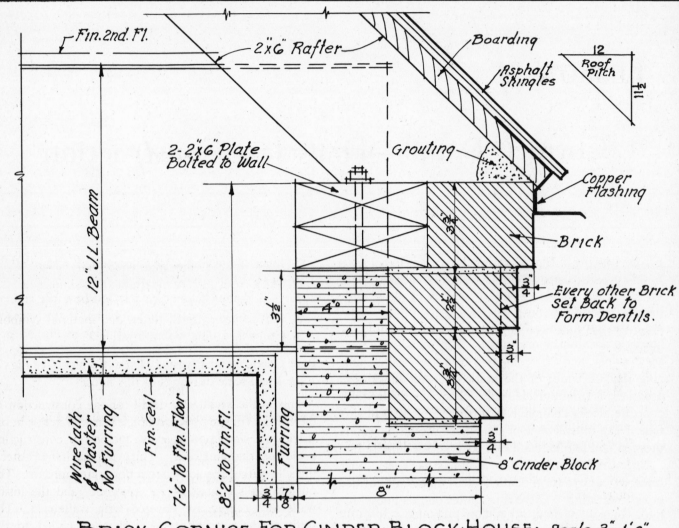

Fin. 2nd. Fl.

2"x6" Rafter

Boarding

Asphalt Shingles

12 Roof Pitch 11½

2-2"x6" Plate Bolted to Wall

Grouting

Copper Flashing

Brick

12" J.L. Beam

3½

Every other Brick Set Back to Form Dentils.

3 4

3½

3"x4"

3"x4"

3 4

Wire lath & Plaster No Furring

Fin. Ceil.

7'-6" to Fin. Floor

8'-2" to Fin. Fl.

Furring

4"

3½

8"

8" Cinder Block

3 4

3 4 7 8

· BRICK · CORNICE · FOR · CINDER · BLOCK · HOUSE · Scale 3"-1'-0"

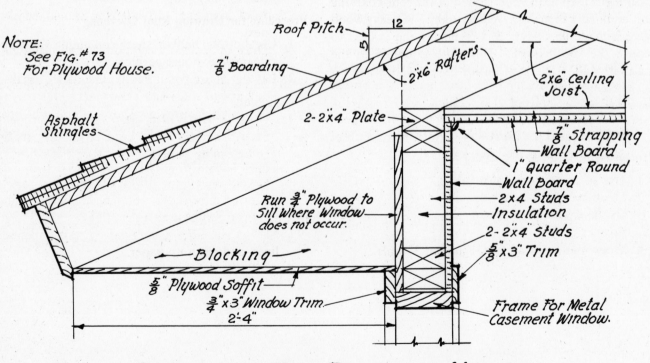

NOTE: See Fig. # 73 For Plywood House.

Roof Pitch

12 5

7 8 " Boarding

2"x6" Rafters

2"x6" Ceiling Joist

Asphalt Shingles

2-2"x4" Plate

7 8 " Strapping
Wall Board
1" Quarter Round
Wall Board
2x4 Studs
Insulation
2- 2"x4" Studs
5 8 "x3" Trim

Run ¾" Plywood to Sill Where Window does not occur.

Blocking

5 8 " Plywood Soffit

¾"x3" Window Trim

2'-4"

Frame For Metal Casement Window.

· ROOF · OVERHANG · FOR · PLYWOOD · HOUSE ·
Scale 1½"-1'-0"

FIGURE 62

77

LESSON 24

Cornice Detail—First-class Construction

The drawing in Fig. 63 shows the cornice detail for a building constructed of brick wall and concrete floor slabs. It is an accurate copy at 3" scale of the full-size detailed drawing that was used to construct this cornice. Some of the things to notice in drawing this cornice are as follows:

1. Solid-brick wall furred on inside with terra-cotta tile to be used as a plaster base. The tile prevents any dampness that may penetrate through the brick wall from reaching the plaster.
2. The concrete floor slab is reinforced with steel rods as shown.
3. The plate is anchored to the concrete with bolts placed at 4'-0" intervals.
4. Blocking is used to build out and make a form for the finished cornice and gutter. As a rule, blocking is just noted on a detail; the construction is left to the carpenter on the job. The architect is interested in the finished cornice only.
5. Copper gutter is built in to form the top member of the cornice. It is held rigid by metal straps, which are fastened to the roof boarding, and a bronze bar along the front of the gutter.
6. The bed mold is used to cover the joint between the soffit and the brick wall. Note the relation of the bed mold to the brick joint.

7. Since this is first-class construction, a slate roof is used.
8. It is common practice not to show the interior finish on a construction drawing of this sort but to make a separate drawing later as the job progresses.

PROBLEM

Procedure for Drawing Cornice Detail (see Fig. 63)

1. Use 12" x 18" sheet.
2. Draw ½" border line and title box.
3. Use 3" scale, and block out very lightly.
4. Draw brick wall first. Outline very lightly.
5. Show concrete work next, with reinforcing rods.
6. Set plate on top of concrete, and show rafters and bolt holding plate to concrete.
7. Roof boarding and blocking should be shown next.
8. Draw in finished wood cornice and metal gutter.
9. Show slate roof and conductor.
10. Put in all dimensions; show material symbols and notes.
11. Go over with a firm, clean line, and outline profile with a heavy line. Erase all unnecessary lines, and clean up paper.

CORNICE DETAIL-IST. CLASS CONST

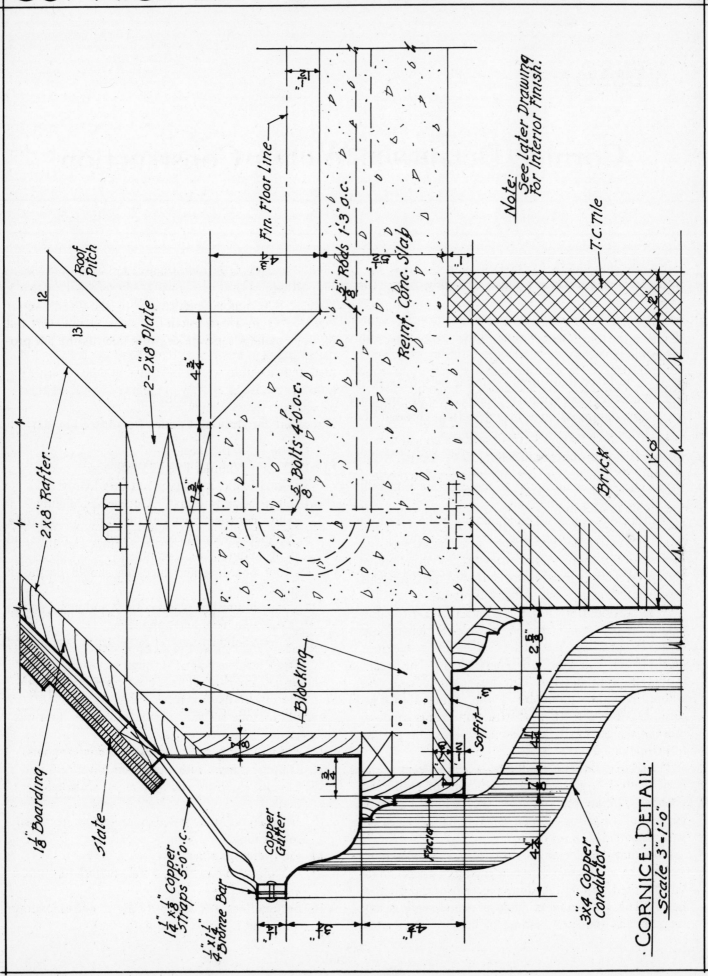

Roof Pitch

12
13

2×8 Rafter

2-2×8 Plate

$4\frac{3}{4}$"

$7\frac{3}{4}$"

Fin. Floor Line

$\frac{5}{8}$" Rods 1'-3" o.c.

$\frac{5}{8}$" Bolts 4'-0" o.c.

Reinf. Conc. Slab

Note: See later Drawing for Interior Finish.

T.C. Tile

Brick

1'-0"

2"

$1\frac{1}{8}$" Boarding

Slate

$1\frac{1}{4}$"×$\frac{1}{8}$" Copper Straps 5'-0" o.c.

$\frac{1}{4}$"×$1\frac{1}{4}$" Bronze Bar

Copper Gutter

Blocking

$\frac{3}{4}$"

$\frac{3}{4}$"

$\frac{3}{8}$"

soffit

Fascia

$2\frac{5}{8}$"

$4\frac{1}{4}$"

$7\frac{1}{8}$"

$4\frac{1}{4}$"

3"×4" Copper Conductor

$1\frac{1}{4}$"

$3\frac{1}{4}$"

$4\frac{1}{2}$"

CORNICE·DETAIL·
Scale 3"=1'-0"

FIGURE 63

LESSON 25

Corner Window

The drawing in Fig. 64 shows a plan, elevation, and section of a corner window and overhanging cornice for a small building. With its concrete roof, floor, and walls, this building could be classed as first-class construction. The design, with its large glass area and overhanging cornice, is in keeping with the present-day modern trend. The exterior walls are made up of stone veneer on concrete or cinder-block backing and are furred and plastered with a marble dado and acoustic soundproof ceiling, as shown in the section.

Most of the drawings in this book are typical details of standard everyday construction, to be copied by the student for practice in drafting and so that he will become familiar with the method, terms, and procedure the architect uses in making his working drawings. If the draftsman becomes proficient in this conventional type of drawing, he should have no difficulty when he comes to the more modern type of construction as shown here. It is safe to predict that in the future this type of construction and design will prevail.

As in previous drawings, this is an actual construction detail, the plan and elevation showing the length and height required and the section showing the thickness of the stock and how it is constructed. This again proves the point that a working drawing is not complete without plan, elevation, and section. They always go together. For the actual construction of this window, most of the sectional views would be drawn in part at full size.

The section shows a reinforced-concrete beam at the head, with a large overhanging cornice of reinforced concrete cantilevered out from the beam. The roof consists of insulating fill on a concrete slab, finished off with a composition roof.

Note that the blocking is fastened to the concrete to receive the metal-covered wood edging. A steel angle lintel is used to hold the stone veneer over the window head. The sash itself is made of wood, with heavy muntins and mullions because of its size. Note that the lower part of the sash opens in. This is shown in the section. The sill and facing below the sill are made up of artificial or cast stone. Note the marble dado and window stool. This marble dado would continue around the room. Note the metal column in the corner of the plan to support the roof at the corner. The plan and elevation would be drawn at a larger scale on a working drawing. They are reduced to ⅛″ scale here to keep the sheets a standard size.

PROBLEM

Procedure for Drawing Corner Window

1. Use 12″ x 18″ sheet or larger.
2. Draw ½″ border and architect's title box.
3. Draw section first at 1″ scale, planning sheet very carefully and drawing with a light, clean line.
4. Draw section through concrete at cornice first, scaling drawing for information where dimensions are not shown.
5. Apply roof finish and blocking with finished nosing.
6. Show angle lintel and stone veneer.
7. Draw head section A through window.
8. Project all material lines down, and draw remainder of sash as shown.
9. Show stone sill and marble dado with floor and terrace lines (section B).
10. Put in all dimensions, notes, material symbols.
11. Go over outline with a clean, firm line.
12. Lay out elevation and plan at ¼″ scale lightly at first.
13. Draw elevation above plan, projecting from plan to elevation.
14. Go over with a firm line.
15. Put on all dimensions, notes, material symbols, and titles.
16. Section lines A-A and B-B refer to corresponding letters on ¾″ scale section.

CORNER WINDOW

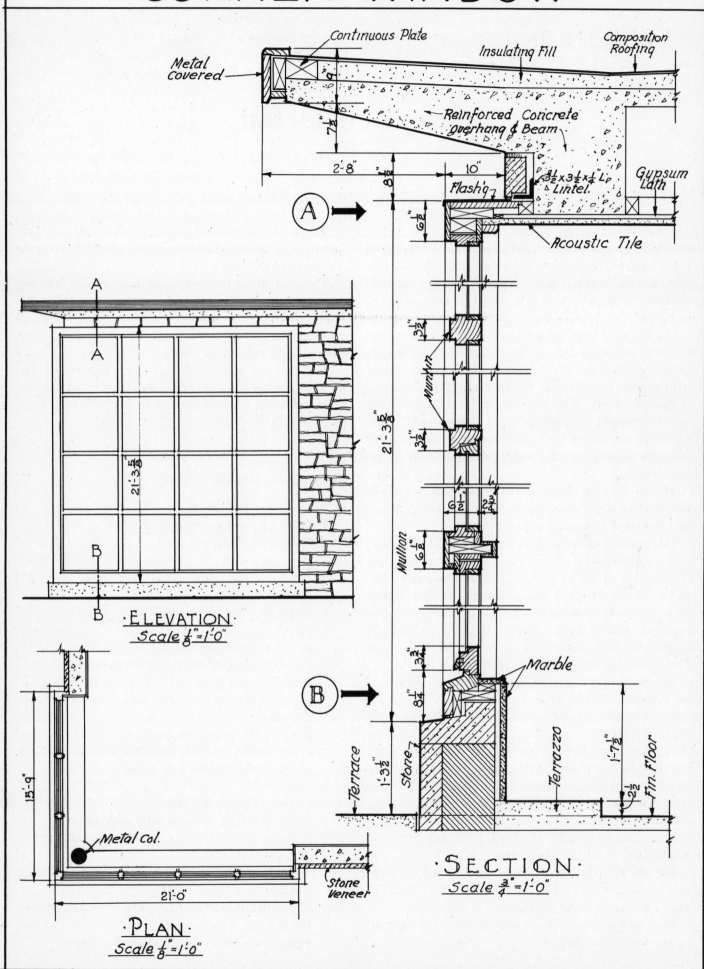

Continuous Plate

Metal covered

Insulating Fill

Composition Roofing

Reinforced Concrete overhang & Beam

9"

7½"

2'-8"

8½"

10"

A →

6½"

Flash'g

3½ x 3½ x ¼" L₀ Lintel.

Gypsum Lath

Acoustic Tile

Mullion

3½"

3½"

6½"

2¾"

6½"

Mullion

21'-3⅝"

21'-3⅝"

B →

3½"

8¼"

Marble

Terrace

Stone

1'-3½"

Terrazzo

Fin. Floor

1'-7½"

2½"

·ELEVATION·
Scale ⅛"=1'-0"

15'-9"

Metal Col.

Stone Veneer

21'-0"

·PLAN·
Scale ⅛"=1'-0"

·SECTION·
Scale ¾"=1'-0"

FIGURE 64

81

LESSON 26

Fireplace Detail

The fireplace, being the central feature of the home, should be given careful consideration. The drawing in Fig. 65 shows the architect's working detail, the familiar plan, section, and elevation, that was used for the construction of the fireplace in the Marshfield house shown in Fig. 84.

The fireplace must be designed with the proper proportions and materials so that fuel will burn readily without sending gas or smoke out into the room. Heat is thrown out by radiation, reflection, and the movement of the heated air. The side walls of the fireplace in the figure are sloped to reflect the heat into the room. Heat would be lost if the side walls ran back straight. In addition, sloping the back wall as shown helps to reflect heat.

The smoke shelf shown in the smoke chamber of the sectional view prevents the smoke from being driven into the room in case of a downdraft.

The amount of opening in the throat will vary with different conditions of the room, the atmosphere, and the location of the house in regard to trees, etc. The height of the chimney has a bearing on this factor, also. When wide open the area of the throat should equal the area of the flue above. A damper should be built in to allow for adjusting the size of the throat. This is nothing more than a large, simple valve.

All dimensions of the fireplace depend on the size of the opening into the room.

The fireplace should be lined with 4″ hard-burned brick or firebrick.

The floor is protected from the heat of the fire by the hearth, which is built of brick, stone, tile, etc. There are several methods of supporting the hearth. The two most common are the reinforced-concrete slab and the one shown here, known as the *trimmer arch*. The back, or inner, hearth is where the fire is built, and the outer hearth extends out into the room.

The ash dump is used to dispose of the ashes by dropping them down to a pit below. This pit has a cleanout door for removing the ashes.

The flue lining is made of terra cotta and is required by law for fire protection.

The brick corbel shown in the ashpit section is the means used to reduce the size of the opening by stepping the brick in gradually.

The plan shows the width and depth of the opening, together with the location of the boiler flue. The elevation shows the height of the opening, the finished mantel, and the wall condition. The section shows the construction behind the surface.

The chimney and fireplace detail is one of the first to be made, for the chimney is built before the framing goes up. The framing should be kept 2″ away from the chimney on all sides.

PROBLEM

Procedure for Drawing Fireplace

1. Use 12″ x 18″″ sheet.
2. Draw ½″ border line and title box.
3. Copy drawing at ¾″ scale.
4. Lay out entire sheet lightly first. Do not complete any one view until entire detail has been blocked out.
5. Draw plan and elevation first.
6. Plan.
   a. Draw rough brickwork and flue first.
   b. Put in finished brick and ash dump.
   c. Show studs, finished wall, and trim.
   d. Put in dimensions, notes, and material symbols.
7. Elevation.
   a. Draw floor line and fireplace opening.
   b. Show trim, mantel, and sheathing.
   c. Put in dimensions and notes.
8. Section.
   a. Draw rough wall first.
   b. Show ashpit, trimmer arch, and hearth.
   c. Draw in brick lining, damper, throat, and 4″ brick front wall.
   d. Show studs, mantel, trim, finish, and sheathing.
   e. Go over with a firm line.
   f. Put in dimensions, notes, and material symbols.
9. Outline all drawings, and put in titles. Erase unnecessary lines, and clean up drawing.

FIREPLACE DETAIL

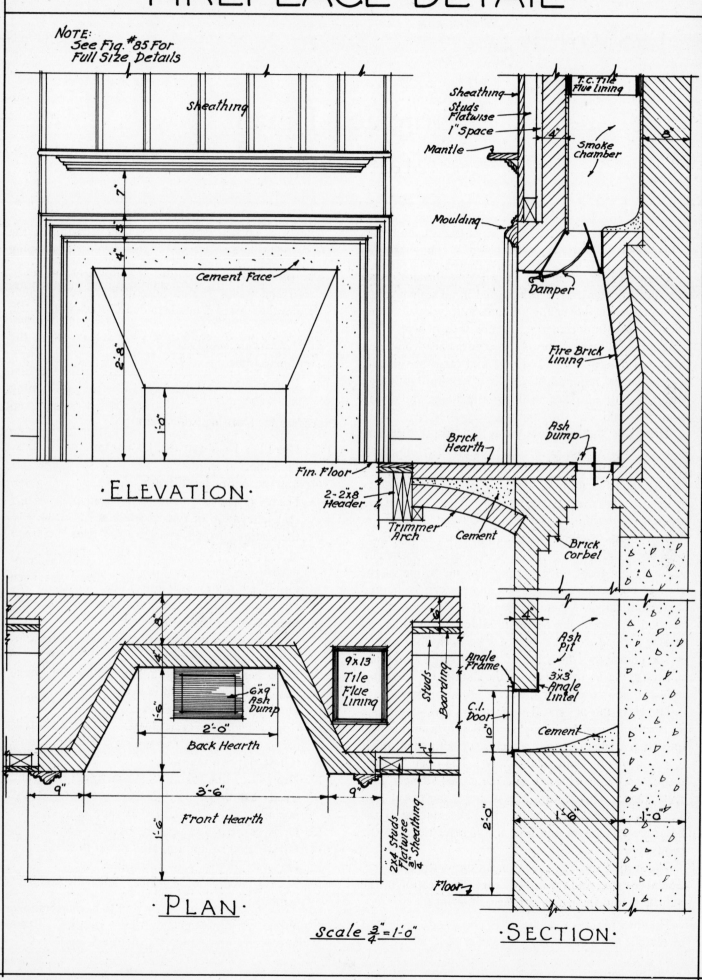

NOTE:
See Fig. #85 For
Full Size Details

Sheathing

Cement Face

7"

3"

4"

2'-8"

1'-0"

·ELEVATION·

T.C. Tile
Flue Lining

Sheathing
Studs
Flatwise
1" Space

Mantle

Moulding

Smoke
Chamber

4"

Damper

Fire Brick
Lining

Ash
Dump

Brick
Hearth

Fin. Floor

2-2"x8"
Header

Trimmer
Arch

Cement

Brick
Corbel

9x13
Tile
Flue
Lining

6"x9"
Ash
Dump

Studs
Boarding

8"

4"

1'-6"

2'-0"

Back Hearth

9"

3'-6"

9"

Front Hearth

1'-6"

2x4 Studs
Flatwise
3/4" Sheathing

·PLAN·

Angle
Frame

C.I.
Door

Ash
Pit

4"

3"x3"
Angle
Lintel

Cement

2'-0"

1'-0"

1'-0"

Floor

·SECTION·

Scale 3/4"=1'-0"

FIGURE 65

83

LESSON 27

Stair Detail

The detail shown in Fig. 66 will give the draftsman the fundamental principles involved in all stair layouts. Although there are many varieties and types of stairs, most of the important factors are shown here. The diagrammatic section shows the required headroom and how it is determined. The riser and tread are shown, as well as the required height for a handrail, although this may vary a little according to the design and conditions involved.

The plans shown below the section are a necessary part of the drawing, as the section alone does not complete the picture. In laying out the risers and treads, the height from floor to floor must be known and the height of the riser decided upon. There are several rules for determining the riser and tread dimensions. For ordinary dwelling houses, a good rule is two risers plus one tread equal 25", $7\frac{1}{2}$" being a good riser height. If the height from floor to floor and the height of the riser to be used are known, the number can be figured mathematically. When the number is determined, the method shown in the geometric diagram (see Fig. 28) can be applied to space the risers between floors.

The plan shows the width of the stairs, the dimension always going to the center of the handrail. The stair indicator shows whether the stairs go up or down.

The elevation of typical stairs shows two conditions, an open and a closed stringer. It is shown in this way only to give the draftsman a picture of both conditions; it would not be built in this way. The open stringer shows the treads exposed, and the closed stringer conceals them. This elevation also shows the newel post and how the handrail ties into it. The spacing of the balusters are shown and how the stringer ties into the room base.

The section through the stringers shows the construction at the wall and the outside edge, the location of the balusters, and the rough carriage, or stringers.

The riser and tread section shows clearly just what the riser and tread are and how they are constructed. Note that the nosing is not included in the width of the tread.

The large-scale details show the design of the handrail and newel post.

PROBLEM

Procedure for Drawing Stair Detail

1. Use 12" x 18" sheet with $\frac{1}{2}$" border and title box. Plan sheet carefully.
2. Lay out entire sheet lightly at first.
3. Draw the diagrammatic section and plans at $\frac{1}{4}$" scale, elevation of typical stairs at $\frac{3}{4}$" scale, and the section through stringers and riser and tread at $1\frac{1}{2}$" scale and full-size details of handrail and newel.
4. Go over outlines with a firm line.
5. Draw diagrammatic section and plans first.
6. Section—draw floor lines first.
7. Lay out risers and treads as shown, using geometric-diagram method.
8. Show headroom, handrails, and floor thickness.
9. Put in all dimensions and notes.
10. Draw plans below as shown.
11. Copy elevation of typical stairs. Refer to details for handrail, newel, and nosing. Handrail must follow slope of stairs.
12. Draw floor line first, and put in rough risers and treads as shown on $\frac{1}{4}$" scale sections. Apply nosings, newel, handrail, and balusters.
13. Draw construction sections next as shown.
14. Draw detail of handrail and newel post.
15. Go over outlines with a firm line.
16. Put in notes, dimensions, and all material symbols.

STAIR DETAIL

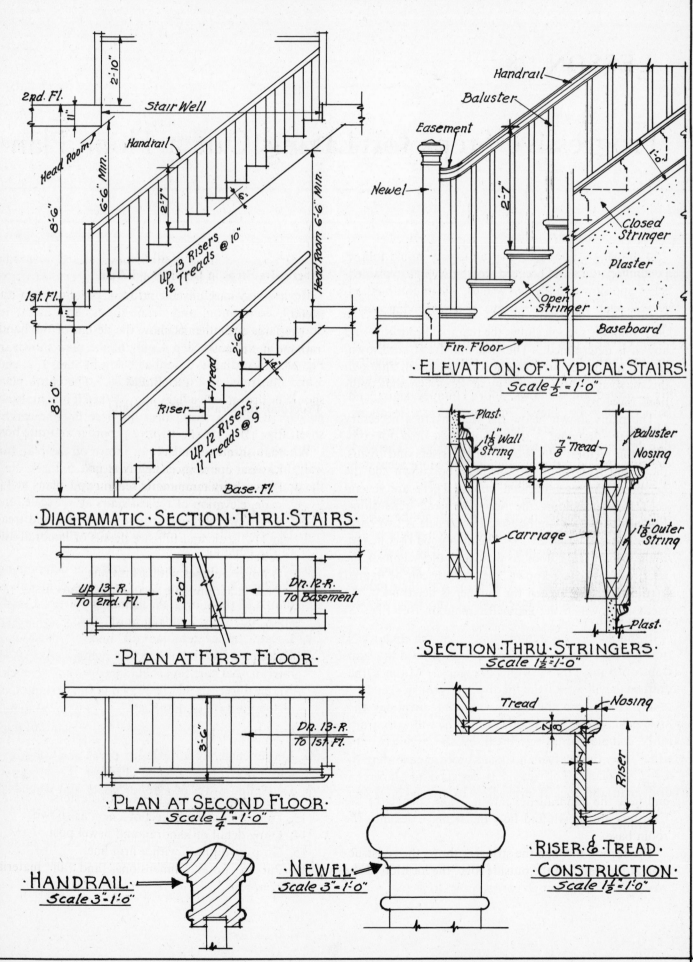

·DIAGRAMATIC·SECTION·THRU·STAIRS·

2nd. Fl.

Stair Well

Head Room

Handrail

2'-10"

8'-6"

6'-6" Min.

2'-7"

6'

1st. Fl.

8'-0"

Up 13 Risers
12 Treads @ 10"

Head Room 6'-6" Min.

2'-6"

Tread

Riser

9"

Up 12 Risers
11 Treads @ 9"

Base. Fl.

·PLAN AT FIRST FLOOR·

Up 13-R.
To 2nd. Fl.

3'-0"

Dn. 12-R.
To Basement

·PLAN AT SECOND FLOOR·
Scale 1/4"=1'-0"

3'-6"

Dn. 13-R.
To 1st. Fl.

·HANDRAIL·
Scale 3"=1'-0"

·NEWEL·
Scale 3"=1'-0"

·ELEVATION·OF·TYPICAL·STAIRS·
Scale 1/2"=1'-0"

Handrail

Baluster

Easement

Newel

2'-7"

Closed
Stringer

Plaster

Open
Stringer

Baseboard

Fin. Floor

·SECTION·THRU·STRINGERS·
Scale 1 1/2"=1'-0"

Plast.

1 1/8" Wall
String

7/8" Tread

Baluster

Nosing

Carriage

1 1/8" Outer
String

Plast.

·RISER·&·TREAD·
·CONSTRUCTION·
Scale 1 1/2"=1'-0"

Tread

Nosing

7/8"

7/8"

Riser

FIGURE 66

85

LESSON 28

Progressive Steps for Laying Out a Floor Plan

In drawing a floor plan the draftsman should follow a definite pattern and proceed step by step as explained below and shown in Figs. 67 and 68. With this method he will soon learn the various steps in laying out a plan.

The essential parts of a plan are the outside wall lines and the positions of the interior partitions, irrespective of doors and windows. After the walls and partitions are indicated, the windows, doors, chimney, stairs, and fixtures may be shown in their correct locations. Always work to center lines of doors, windows, and like details, instead of working to the sides. The work can thus be laid out more rapidly and more accurately than by working to the side lines.

The plan may look very complicated to a beginner; but if it is broken down and analyzed as to the various steps a contractor would follow in construction, the picture will become much clearer. The draftsman should try to visualize what the finished product will look like. Practice in copying plans with their indications, symbols, and conventions is the best way to acquire skill.

It should be understood that it is the architect's function to develop plans and designs; the draftsman transforms these into working drawings. At times, the draftsman will work from the architect's rough sketches, taking from them the dimensions and directions the architect conceived. At other times, he will work from fairly complete drawings made by the architect. In either case, the draftsman should proceed according to a logical plan. This lesson is designed to show the draftsman the logical procedure to follow in laying out a floor plan. Lesson 29 will be devoted to elevations.

PROBLEM

Progressive Steps in Developing a Plan

Review very carefully the information shown on the symbol, convention, and detail sheets, and use it in drawing this and other plans.

Draw at ¼" scale Step 4 only of the plan shown in Fig. 68, proceeding as described below in Steps 1, 2, and 3 and illustrated in Figs. 67 and 68. The entire plan should be drawn with a light line. When it is completed go over it with a clean, firm line (see line-indication sheet, Fig. 13).

Where the dimensions are not shown on the plan for wall thickness, openings, stairs, fireplace, fixtures, etc., the draftsman may measure with his scale.

Step 1 (see Fig. 67)

  a. Draw outside wall lines the total length and width of the building.
  b. Draw inside line of exterior wall after determining thickness by material to be used. A stud wall is drawn 6" thick over all, including plaster, 2" x 4" studs, boarding, and wall finish.
  c. Locate by center line all interior partitions. Determine width, and draw in lightly. A 2" x 4" interior stud partition should be drawn 5½" thick. All partitions should be drawn in full, irrespective of the position of doors, etc.

Step 2 (see Fig. 67)

  a. Locate center of all exterior doors and windows, and draw a center line through these points.
  b. Determine width of exterior doors and windows, and show with proper indications (see convention sheet, Fig. 47).
  c. Locate interior door openings, draw in proper width, and erase partition lines in openings.

PROGRESSIVE STEPS-PLAN

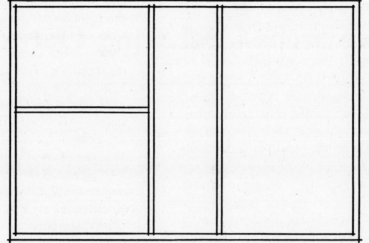

·STEP· ①

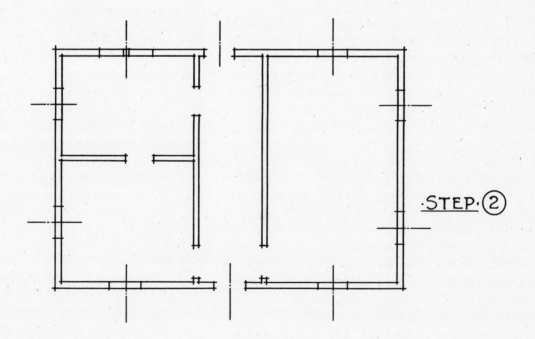

·STEP· ②

52
31'6"

FIGURE 67

87

Step 3 (see Fig. 68)

    a. Locate and draw in fireplace, chimney, and flue (see fireplace detail, Fig. 65).

    b. Stairs should be drawn next, with partitions in relation to them, care being taken to allow sufficient headroom. A section should be made to determine this. The stairs must be figured out and drawn according to the height from floor to floor and the dimensions for risers and treads (see stair detail, Fig. 66).

    c. Show door swings.

    d. Kitchen equipment should be drawn in next, including counters, cupboards, sink, refrigerator, and range.

    e. Draw in front and rear steps and porch, if house has one.

Step 4 (see Fig. 68)

    a. Locate electric-light outlets, switches, and base plugs, and indicate with proper symbols (see electric symbols, Fig. 45).

    b. Draw the exterior over-all dimension lines and also the subordinate dimension lines, locating the window and door openings and the projections or breaks in the wall surfaces in the plan. All openings are dimensioned to centers. Use arrowheads at ends of dimension lines. Also run a dimension line through the plan in each direction, locating the main partitions of the building. The dimensions are taken from the outside face of the exterior studs to the center of interior partitions. The dimensions determine the size of rooms, halls, etc.

    c. Letter in the title of the plan, scale, indication of materials, room titles, and any fixtures requiring notes. Also, mark the size of doors. Door sizes are determined largely by their location. Generally, the exterior main entrance door is 2'-10" to 3'-0" wide. Rear entrance and interior doors to rooms are 2'-6" wide. Closet doors, except in special cases, are 2'-4" wide.

    d. Other floor plans of the same building should be traced over the first-floor plan to establish walls, bearing partitions, etc.

PROGRESSIVE STEPS-PLAN

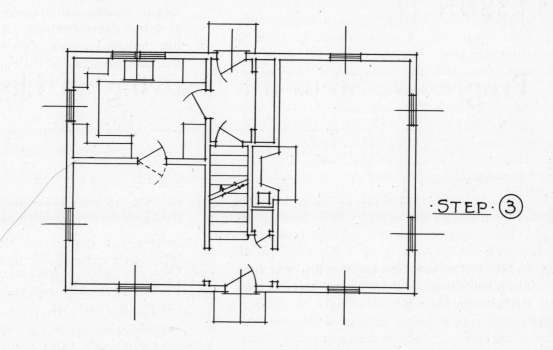

·STEP· ③

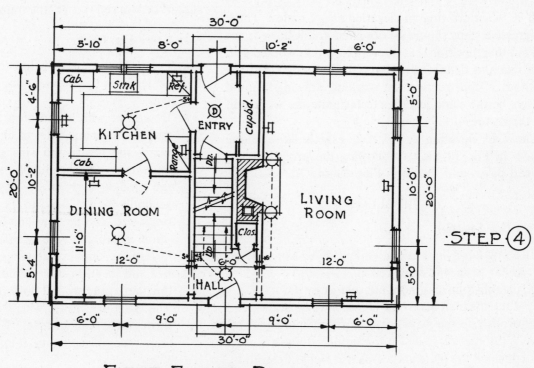

·STEP· ④

FIRST·FLOOR·PLAN·
scale ⅛"=1'-0"

FIGURE 68

89

LESSON 29

Progressive Steps for Drawing an Elevation

For this lesson it is assumed that the design has been decided upon and all the necessary information compiled. There are many details to consider before proceeding with the drawings, such as floor and ceiling heights, sill construction, plate height and cornice construction, pitch of roof and type of gutter, type of doors and windows and their location, height of chimney, flashing, and conductors. The larger and more complicated the building, the more details there are to consider.

Figure 70 shows a complete elevation with all the necessary information to proceed with this lesson.

Carefully study and refer when necessary to Figs. 69 and 70 when drawing an elevation at $\frac{1}{4}''$ scale. These progressive steps should be observed and followed, not only in this elevation, but in every elevation worked out. The size and detail may vary with the design, but the method of constructing the working drawings should always be the same in order to facilitate the work and get the best results.

Draw an elevation at $\frac{1}{4}''$ scale exactly like the one shown in Fig. 70, Step 4, following the procedure described below and shown in Figs. 69 and 70.

PROBLEM

Step 1 (see Fig. 69)

a. Draw floor lines as shown and dimensioned from cellar to second-floor ceiling.
b. Establish finish grade line, and draw it.
c. Tack the plan below the elevation to be drawn, and project up the main corners of the building.
d. With the necessary information, draw a section through the plate and cornice at right of elevation, and project cornice lines and ridge of roof over to elevation (see cornice details, Fig. 60).

The cornice and roof are then blocked out with light lines. The pitch and shape of the roof are determined by the design and effect desired and should work out correctly with the width of the side elevation and the height of the ridge line. The positions of the main cornice lines are determined by the construction as worked out at the plate and the foot of the rafters. Approximately, the top cornice line should be about level with the top of the attic floor joists. The detail lines of the cornice are to be worked out later; only the main lines should be worked out at this time.

Step 2 (see Fig. 69)

a. From plan tacked below elevation, project up center lines of chimney, door, and window openings.
b. Determine widths and draw in jamb lines of door and windows and sides of chimney.
c. Draw the heads and sills of door and window openings. The height of these is determined by the design and effect desired. Windows are generally dimensioned to the top of the sash. All stock sizes can be obtained from a stock-sash and -door catalogue (see window detail, Fig. 56).
d. Determine height of chimney and draw cap. The size and location of a chimney are determined by the plan at the second floor or just under the roof. The section shows where the chimney comes through the roof surface.
e. Show top of concrete foundation and concrete step.

PROGRESSIVE STEPS-ELEVATION

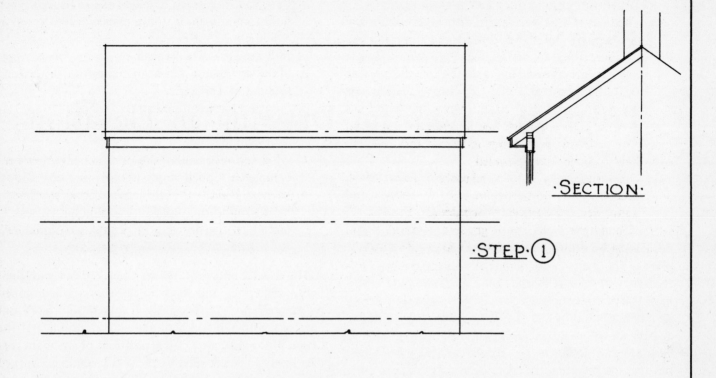

·SECTION·

·STEP· ①

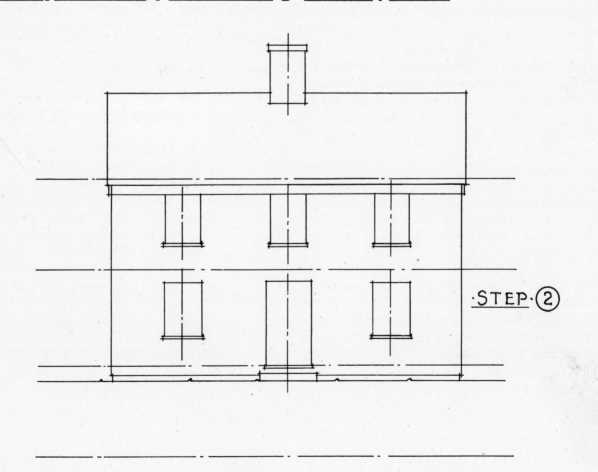

·STEP· ②

FIGURE 69

Step 3 (see Fig. 70)

   a. Draw trim around door and window openings.

   b. The lines of window frames, sash, and muntins are next drawn and the doorhead and door worked out according to design. At ¼″ scale a single line indicates the *muntins*, a double line the meeting rail. Draw the side and top rails 1½″ wide and the bottom rail 2½″ wide. Draw the wood sill 2″ wide with a double line to indicate the *wash*. Any peculiarities of design in frames and sash will have to be specially detailed.

   c. Draw the cornice profiles and molding lines clearly, according to the particular style of cornice and gutter decided on (see cornice details, Fig 60).

   d. Foundation walls below grade are invisible and must be drawn with a dotted line (see Fig. 70).

Step 4 (see Fig. 70)

   a. Put in all necessary dimensions for floor heights, floor to grade, floor to top of sash, ridge to top of chimney.

   b. Indicate glass size on sash.

   c. Show conductor pipes and cast-iron drains and foundation for step.

   d. Show and note all necessary flashing.

   e. Show indication for finished material for walls, roof, chimney, etc.

   f. All descriptive lines of the elevation have now been completed. Such notes as are necessary should be neatly and carefully lettered, the lettering to be in proportion, uniform in height and style, and placed on the drawing in positions to look well. Repeat the notes only where necessary.

PROGRESSIVE STEPS-ELEVATION

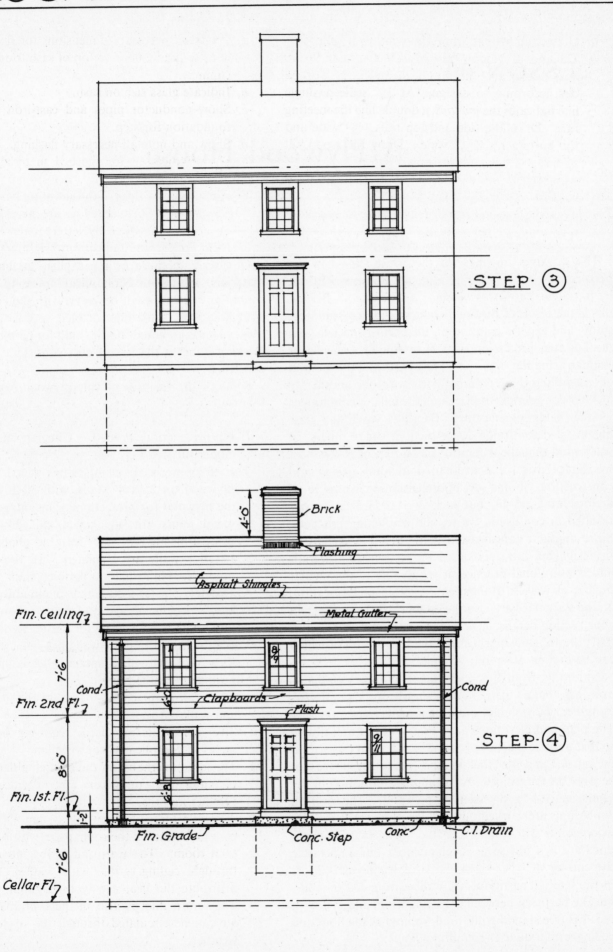

·STEP·③

Brick

Flashing

Asphalt Shingles

Metal Gutter

Fin. Ceiling

7'-6"

Cond.

Fin. 2nd Fl.

Clapboards

Flash

Cond

·STEP·④

8'-0"

Fin. 1st Fl.

-2"

Fin. Grade

Conc. Step

Conc

C.I. Drain

7'-6"

Cellar Fl.

FIGURE 70

93

LESSON 30

A Plywood House

The working drawings for the house shown in the perspective sketch (see Fig. 71) have been worked out by a system known as *modular coordination*. Briefly, this is the result of thorough and painstaking planning, study, and experimentation on the part of specialists in the building profession who have sought a means of standardizing the sizes of building parts and the method of assembling these different parts with one another.

After considerable research on the part of committees in the fields of masonry, flooring, windows, glass block, skeleton-frame construction, and others, it was found that the 4″ unit of measurement is the most workable basis for coordinating building design and construction. Some sort of dimensioning is used in all architectural design, but lack of standardization has resulted in confusion, waste, and conflicting practices. Since modular coordination is not a radical departure in design but is rather based on established materials and conventional practice, it is valuable to the regular builder as well as to those interested in prefabrication.

The system is based on the established sizes of certain construction details, such as the common brick, 2″ x 4″ x 8″; the 16″ stud spacing; and the 12″ rule, all of which can be broken down into 4″ units.

Naturally, from this many other multiples of the 4″ unit are built. The house, shown in Fig. 71, for example, has been laid out on a modular base of 4 feet. The plan and elevations have been planned and drawn so that a stock sheet of plywood (4′ x 8′) can be used on the outside and the stock-sized sheets of wallboard can be used on the inside. All windows are located in the center of a 4′ x 8′ sheet of plywood. The over-all dimensions are worked out in 4′ lengths so that the plywood joints will come on a stud. The interior partitions are laid out so as to eliminate as far as possible the cutting of stock-sized sheets of wallboard. Most of the interior partitions are wallboard nailed to studs, but the partition between the living room and bedroom No. 1 is free standing plywood, secured at the floor and ceiling with a quarter-round molding.

Obviously, because of the savings in labor and in materials, this is an economical house to build. It should not be confused, however, with the cheap jerry-built houses of some unprincipled speculator-contractors. This is an honest house, built for permanence and modern living at the lowest cost consistent with good construction.

Some of the features of this plywood house are as follows:

1. No excavation needed. Concrete floor is on cinder fill (see Fig. 54).
2. Exterior walls are of ¾″ stock 4′ x 8′ sheets of plywood on 2″ x 4″ studs, with 30-lb. felt under the plywood for protection against moisture. Plywood joints are ³⁄₁₆″ apart, calked with a gun using a mastic that stays soft and pliable.
3. Exterior walls are insulated with rock wool or other suitable insulation between studs.
4. The only plaster used is that required by fire regulations in the garage and heater room. Therefore, there is no waiting for plaster to dry.
5. Wallboard on interior walls has filled joints, or if sheet rock is used, a special filler is applied and wallpaper can be hung.
6. Studs can be placed 2′-0″ o.c. to receive plywood and wallboards.
7. Steel casements are used, requiring no window boxes or complicated construction.
8. The large overhang on the roof eliminates the use of gutter and conductors and provides shade in summer months.
9. A simple forced-air heating system supplies heat by a main duct in the roof space, with branches to each room. The warm air is fed into the room through ceiling grills with baffles that help distribute the heat evenly throughout the room. The return duct is also in the roof space. Cool air can be circulated through this system in hot weather.

FIGURE 71. A plywood house

PROBLEM

Procedure for Drawing Plywood House (see Figs. 72 to 74)

1. Use 12″ x 18″ sheet for each drawing.
2. The drawing should be done lightly at first; afterward the entire layout should be gone over with a firm, clear line.
3. Draw a ½″ border line and title box.
4. Use dimensions where shown, scaling only where figures are not given.   Draw at ¼″ scale.   Draw cornice and sill details at 1½″ scale (see Figs. 62 and 54).
5. For drawing purposes, show outside walls 6″, interior stud partitions 5″, and plywood partitions with no studs 1½″ thick.
6. In drawing elevations and section, refer to the sill section (Fig. 54) and cornice section (Fig. 62).
7. Following the procedure described and shown in progressive steps for drawing plans and elevations (Figs. 67 to 70), draw each of the working drawings shown.
8. Put in dimension lines as shown, and add all dimensions, notes, center lines, and titles.

These working drawings—the floor plan, front elevation, rear elevation, end elevations, cross section, and details, with an outline specification describing the work—would be the contract set.

PLYWOOD HOUSE

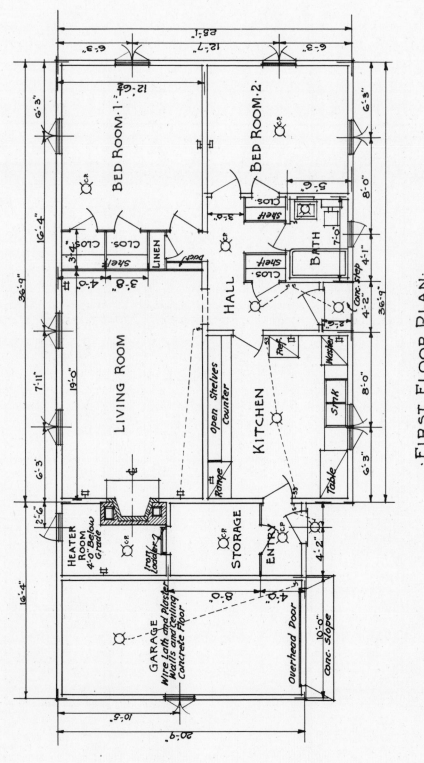

·FIRST FLOOR PLAN·
Scale ⅛" = 1'·0"

·DOOR·WIDTHS·

Front   3'-0"
Entry   2'-8"
Rooms   2'-6"
Closets   2'-4"
Bath   2'-4"
Linen   2'-0"

FIGURE 72

97

PLYWOOD HOUSE

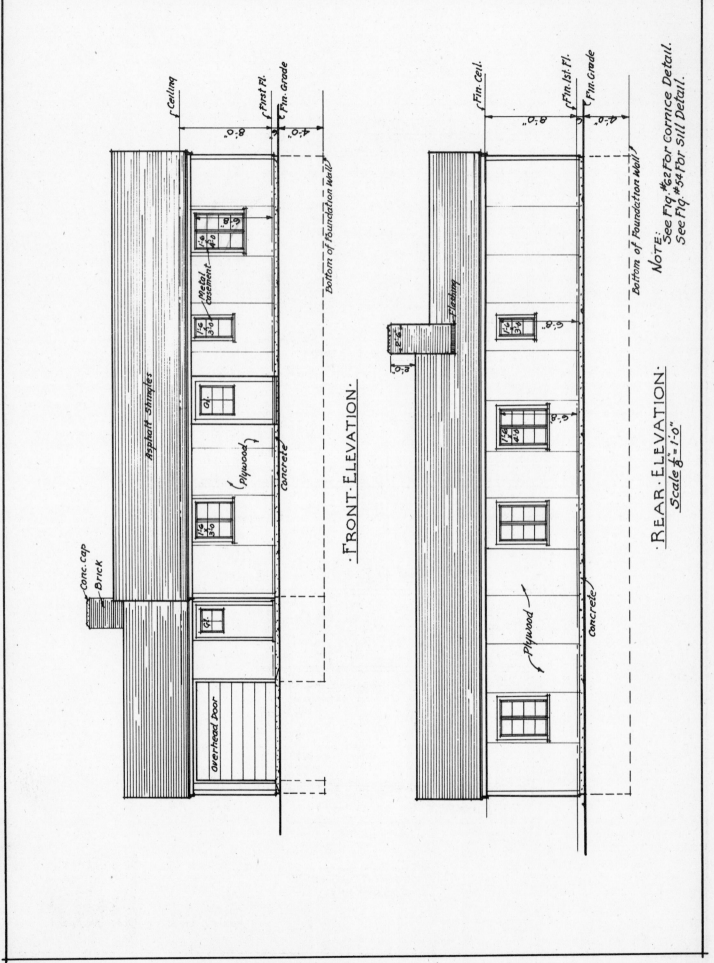

FRONT·ELEVATION·

·REAR·ELEVATION·
Scale ⅛" = 1'-0"

NOTE:
See Fig. #62 For Cornice Detail.
See Fig. #54 For Sill Detail.

FIGURE 73

98

PLYWOOD HOUSE

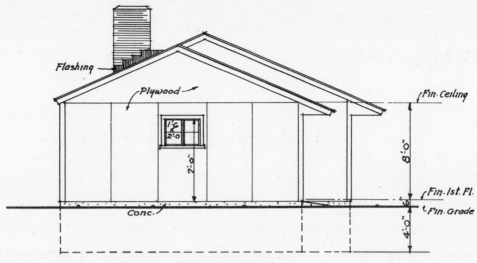

Flashing
Plywood
Fin. Ceiling
$\frac{1'-6}{2'-0}$
7'-0"
8'-0"
Fin. 1st. Fl.
Conc.
Fin. Grade
4'-0"

· END · ELEVATION ·

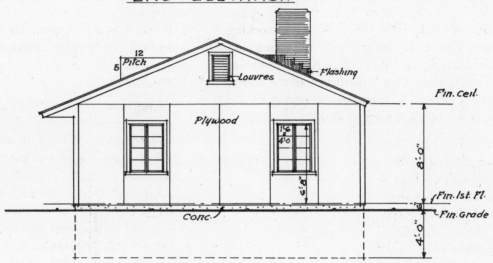

12
5
Pitch
Louvres
Flashing
Fin. Ceil.
Plywood
$\frac{1'-6}{4'-0}$
6'-8"
8'-0"
Fin. 1st. Fl.
Conc.
Fin. Grade
4'-0"

· END · ELEVATION ·
Scale $\frac{1}{8}" = 1'-0"$

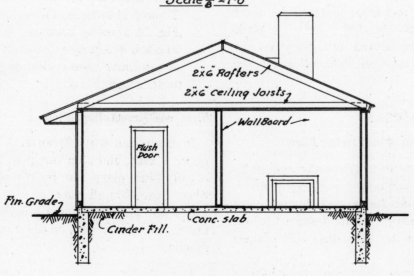

2"x6" Rafters
2"x6" Ceiling Joists
WallBoard
Flush Door
Fin. Grade
Cinder Fill.
Conc. slab

· CROSS · SECTION ·
Scale $\frac{1}{8}" = 1'-0"$

NOTE:
See Fig. #54 For Sill Section.
See Fig. #62 For Cornice Section.

FIGURE 74

LESSON 31

The Marshfield House

The following drawings make up a complete set of working drawings for the construction of the house shown in the photographs (Figs. 75 and 76). They are exact ⅛″ scale reproductions of the ¼″ scale working drawings that were used for competitive figuring and for the construction of the house. A few full-size details were made during the construction of the house, to complete the job. The drawings that made up the contract set as shown here are as follows:

Basement Plan—Fig. 77.
First-floor plan—Fig. 78.
Second-floor plan—Fig. 79.
Front elevation—Fig. 80.
End elevations—Fig. 81.
Rear elevation—Fig. 82.
Framing plans—Fig. 83.
Living-room details—Fig. 84.
Full-size details—Fig. 85.

The drawings will be explained in the order listed above and should be drawn in that order. The plans and elevations should be blocked out lightly first, no one drawing being completed until all have been blocked out.

PROBLEM

Procedure for Drawing Marshfield House Plans

1. Use 12″ x 18″ sheets with ½″ border and architect's title box.
2. Draw floor plans, elevations, and framing plans at ¼″ scale, following procedure described below.
3. Draw separate plan on each sheet. Plan sheet very carefully.
4. Draw front and rear elevations on separate sheets and two end elevations on one sheet.
5. Draw two framing plans on one sheet.
6. Draw living-room elevation on one sheet at ¾″ scale.

7. Draw full-size sections on one sheet.
8. Check all figures and cross-reference notes very carefully.
9. When drawing is complete, clean up all sheets, and fill in title boxes and date.

Basement Plan

1. Using dimensions given and following the progressive steps for laying out a plan (see Figs. 67 and 68), draw the outline of the basement plan. Where dimensions are not given, measure with the scale, using ⅛″ = 1'-0″.
2. After outline has been drawn, show stairs, chimney, Lally columns, windows, and areas.
3. Draw in all extension and dimension lines.
4. Do not put dimensions, notes, or room titles on drawing until other plans and elevations are blocked out.
5. Note that over-all dimension of basement wall is 2″ more than figure shown on first-floor plan (see Fig. 52, showing concrete wall out 1″ from frame to allow boarding to be flush with concrete wall). Wood-frame construction is always dimensioned to the rough frame.

First- and Second-floor Plans

In laying out work in an architect's office, tracing paper is used, and after one plan is drawn the outline of all other plans can be traced. For schoolwork where heavy Manila paper is used, each plan and elevation will have to be laid out separately. Although this requires more work on the student's part, it is good practice.

1. From dimensions given, draw outline of building very lightly.
2. Follow procedure described and shown for progressive steps in laying out a plan (see Figs. 67 and 68.

FIGURE 75 Marshfield house, front view

FIGURE 76 Marshfield house, rear view

3. Note that the over-all dimensions for first floor are less than for basement.
4. Use dimensions where shown, scale-drawing only when dimensions are not given. Window widths should be figured out from elevations.
5. All outside walls should be drawn 6″ thick.
6. Draw all interior partitions 5½″ thick.
7. Refer to various details of stairs, fireplace, windows, etc., when drawing plan.
8. Refer to symbol, convention, and line-indication sheet.
9. Show dimension lines only. Do not dimension until elevations are blocked out.

Elevations

Do not draw any one elevation complete until all have been blocked out. The end elevations must be drawn in conjunction with the front and rear to establish the height of ridge, cornice, etc.

1. Follow procedure for drawing elevation (see Figs. 69 and 70).
2. See Fig. 56 for window detail and Fig. 52 for sill detail.
3. See Fig. 58 for main-entrance-door detail and Fig. 60 for cornice detail.
4. Over-all lengths and center of windows can be projected from the plans. Size of windows can be figured out by the glass size given and the number of lights shown.
5. Slope of roof is determined by the pitch shown on the end elevations.
6. After all elevations are blocked out, indicate materials by proper symbols. Put on all notes, dimensions, and titles.
7. Go over elevations with a clean, firm line, and outline profile as shown.
8. Go over outline of plans, and put in all dimensions, notes, and titles.

Framing Plans

Most towns and cities require separate framing plans as shown in Fig. 83, but in some cases the framing can be indicated on the floor plan. It is well to make a separate plan as shown here to give the contractor a clear picture, making it easier to figure the job and build by. Some cities require wall-framing drawings with a set of plans, but this is so rare that it will not be discussed here. The building code of the specific locality should be studied carefully, for many codes specify the size of lumber, etc., required to be used for framing.

1. Draw framing plans as shown here, drawing outline first of first floor.
2. Draw sill, main beams, and Lally columns.

3. Show floor joists and bridging, spacing floor joists as indicated.
4. Put on all notes.
5. Follow same procedure for second-floor framing, showing main beams first.

¾″ Scale Details

The elevation of the living-room wall shows a detailed picture of the end of the living room. This detail with the full-size sections (see Figs. 84 and 85) gives the contractor all the information needed to figure and install this work. It also gives the mill the information needed to mill out the stock. To draw this detail, proceed as follows, with a light line:

1. Draw floor and ceiling lines first. In drawing from this detail, all figures and information are given. To lay out and draw a detail like this, the draftsman must get his information from the plan and elevations and draw the detail to meet the conditions.
2. From figures given, draw fireplace opening.
3. Section lines with letters referring to corresponding letters on full-size detail sheet (see Fig. 85).
4. Referring to sections *C* and *A* on full-size detail sheet, draw molding around fireplace opening and mantel shelf.
5. Using figures and full-size sections, draw window, cupboards, bookcases, cornice, and sheathing.
6. Go over with a clean, firm line, and outline as shown.
7. Put in all notes and dimensions. Show title and scale.

Full-size Details

This sheet shows the full-size profile of the molding used in the ¾″ scale detail of the living-room wall. They are drawn at full size so that the mill can grind its knives and reproduce the moldings exactly as designed by the architect. Any variation in the making of the moldings would be likely to change the whole character of the room.

The section letters refer to the section lines on the ¾″ scale detail (see Fig. 84).

In drawing these details, block them out very carefully and sketch out the moldings very lightly over and over again until the exact profile is obtained (see molding sheet, Fig. 41).

The ¾″ scale detail picture gives the length of the molding required, and the full-size section gives the sectional view. One is of no value to the contractor without the other; the two drawings must go together to make a complete picture.

When profiles are perfected, go over with a firm line and crosshatch to make a clearer picture.

MARSHFIELD HOUSE- PLAN

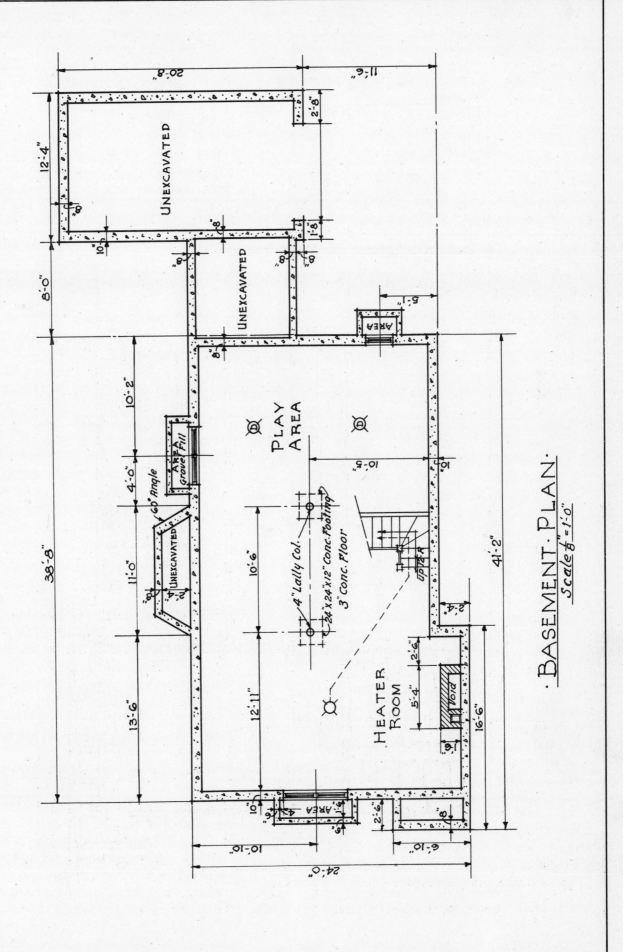

UNEXCAVATED

UNEXCAVATED

UNEXCAVATED

AREA
Gravel Fill

60° Angle

AREA

PLAY
AREA

4" Lally Col.

24"x24"x12" Conc.Footing
3" Conc. Floor

UPPER

HEATER
ROOM

Void

AREA

·BASEMENT·PLAN·
Scale ⅛"=1'-0"

FIGURE 77

103

MARSHFIELD HOUSE - PLAN

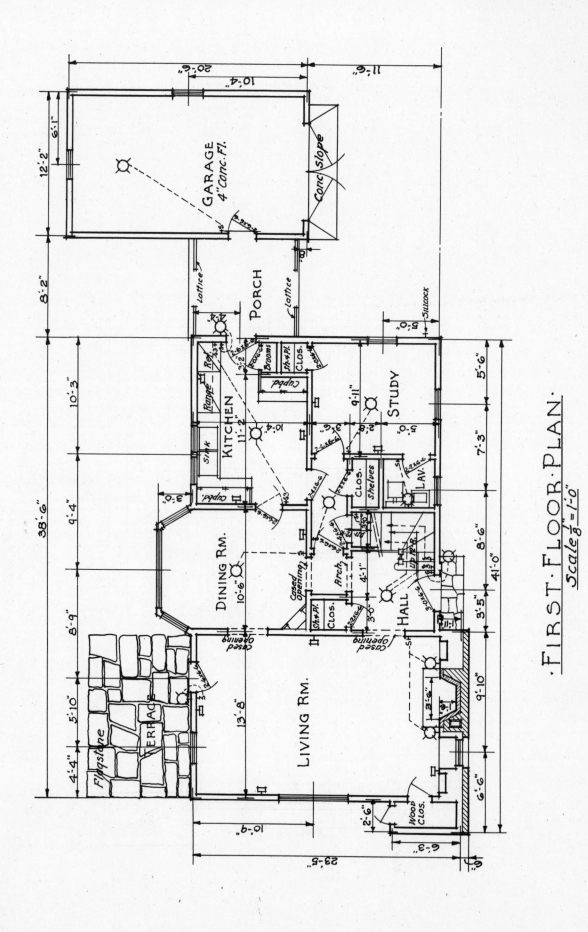

FIRST·FLOOR·PLAN·
Scale $\frac{1}{8}$"=1'-0"

FIGURE 78

104

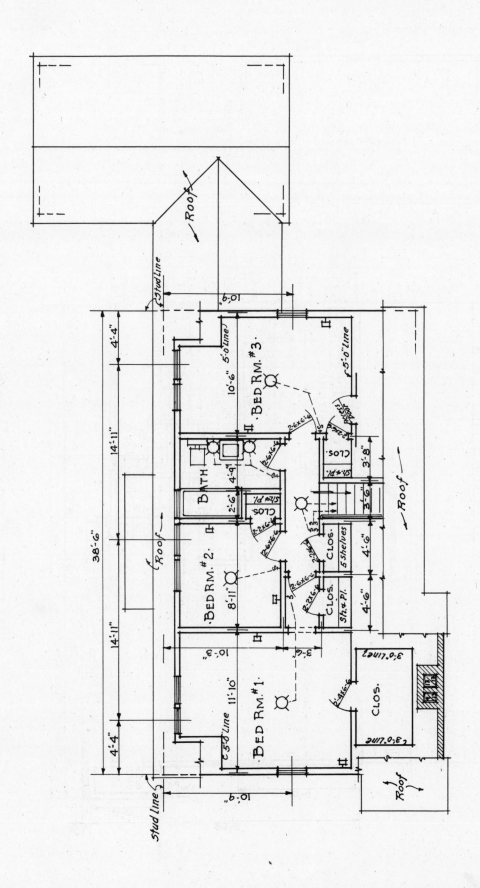

·SECOND·FLOOR·PLAN·
Scale $\frac{1}{8}$"=1'-0"

FIGURE 79

105

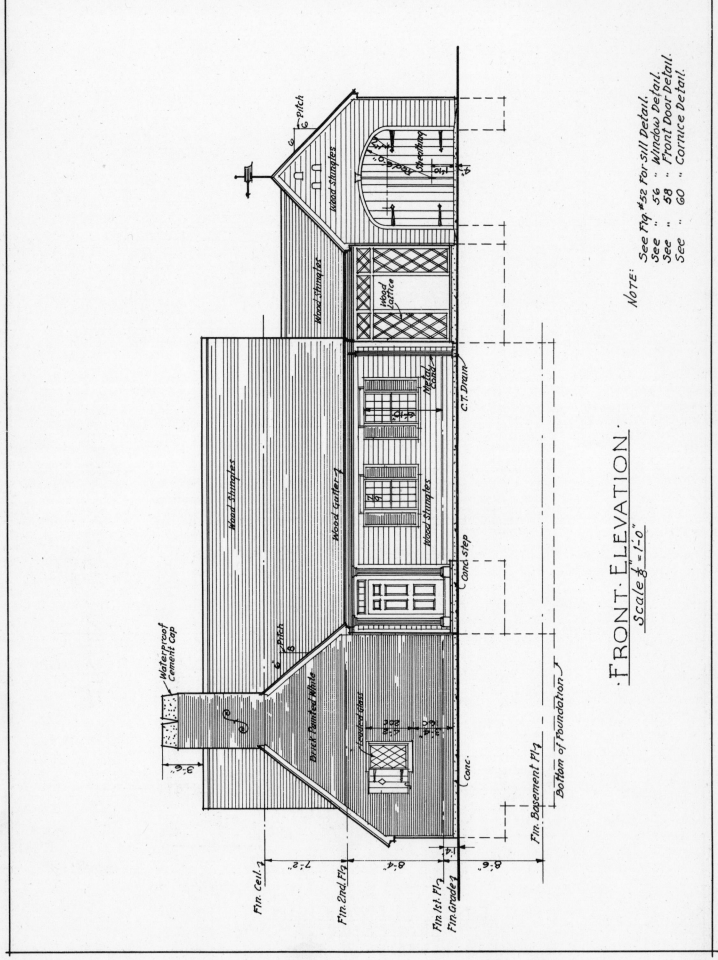

·FRONT· ELEVATION·
Scale ⅛"= 1'-0"

NOTE: See Fig. #52 For sill Detail.
See " 56 " Window Detail.
See " 58 " Front Door Detail.
See " 60 " Cornice Detail.

FIGURE 80

106

MARSHFIELD HOUSE-ELEVATION

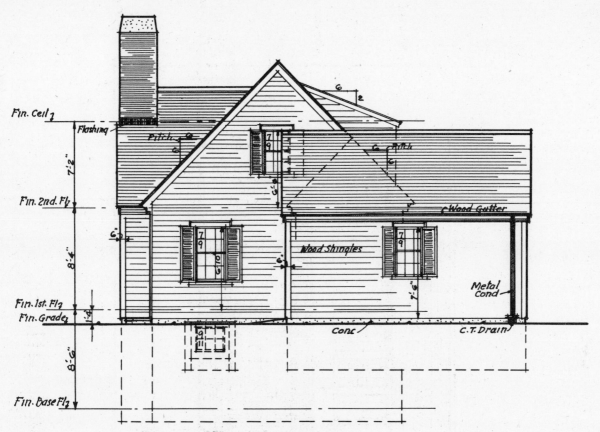

· END · ELEVATION ·
Scale ⅛"=1'-0"

· END · ELEVATION ·
Scale ⅛"=1'-0"

FIGURE 81

107

·REAR·ELEVATION·
Scale ⅛"=1'·0"

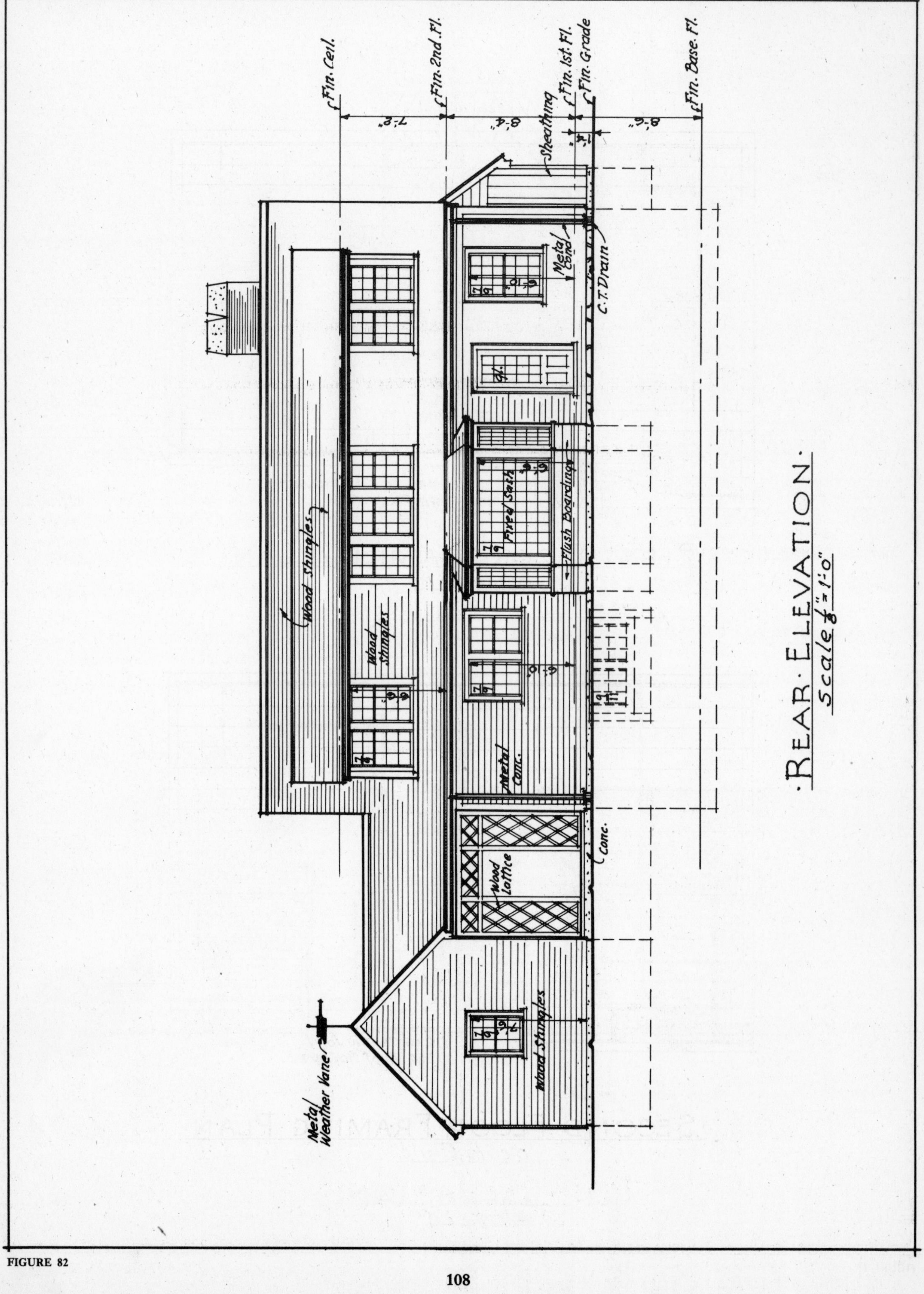

FIGURE 82

108

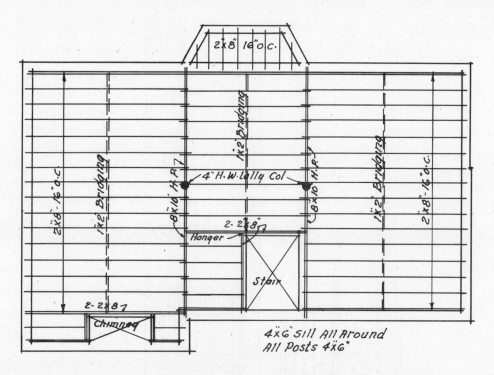

·First·Floor·Framing·Plan·
Scale ⅛"=1:0"

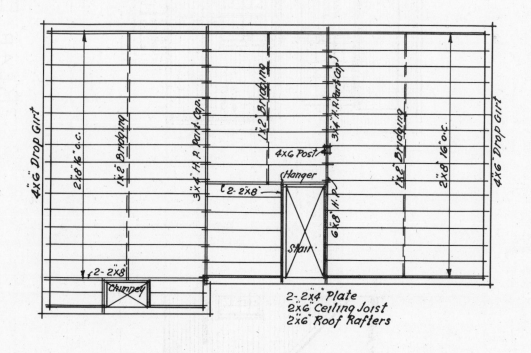

·Second·Floor·Framing·Plan·
Scale ⅛"=1:0"

FIGURE 83

109

MARSHFIELD HOUSE - ¾" DETAILS

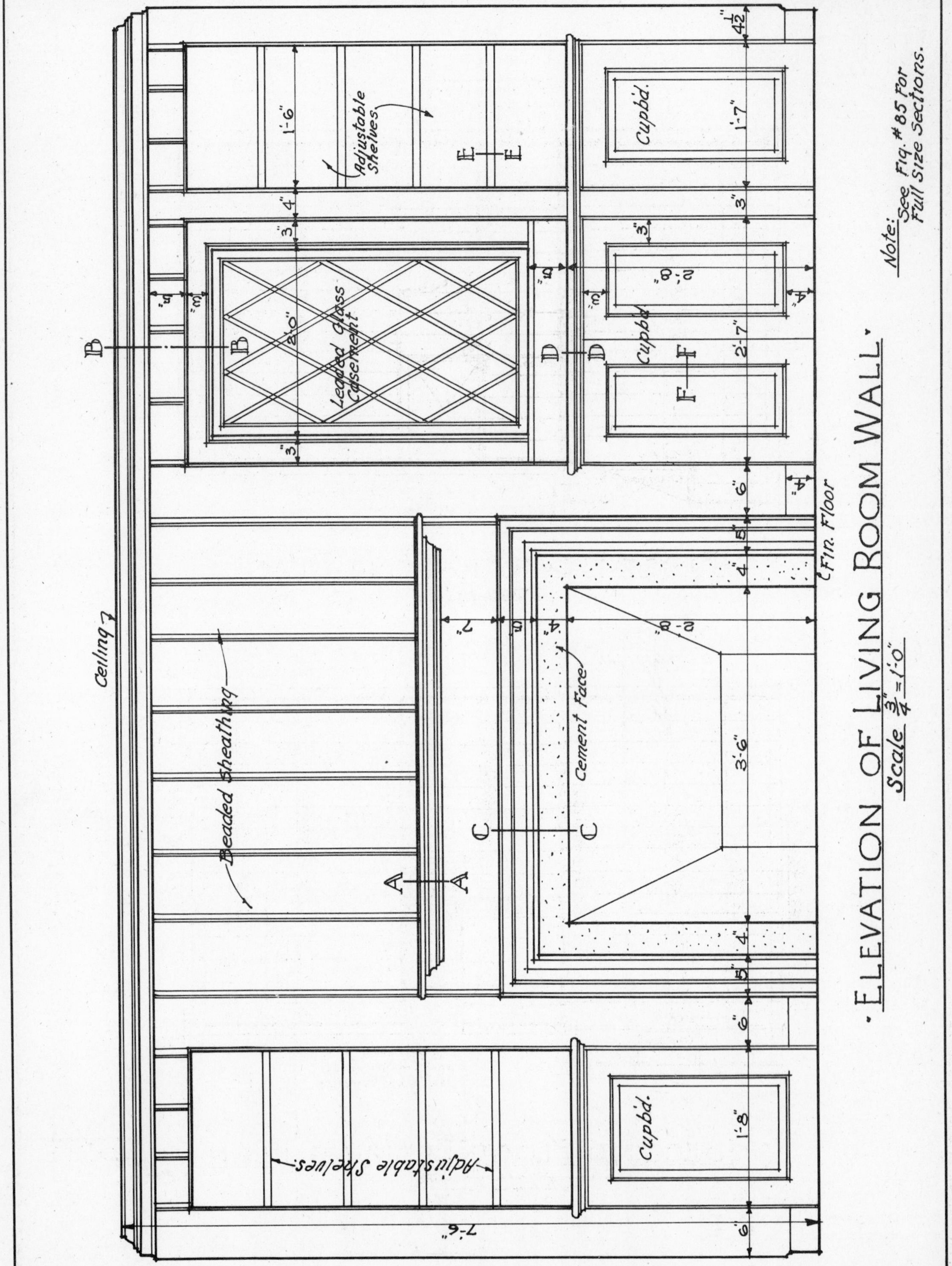

ELEVATION OF LIVING ROOM WALL.
Scale ¾"=1'-0"

Note: See Fig. #85 for Full Size Sections.

FIGURE 84

110

MARSHFIELD HOUSE-F·S·DETAILS

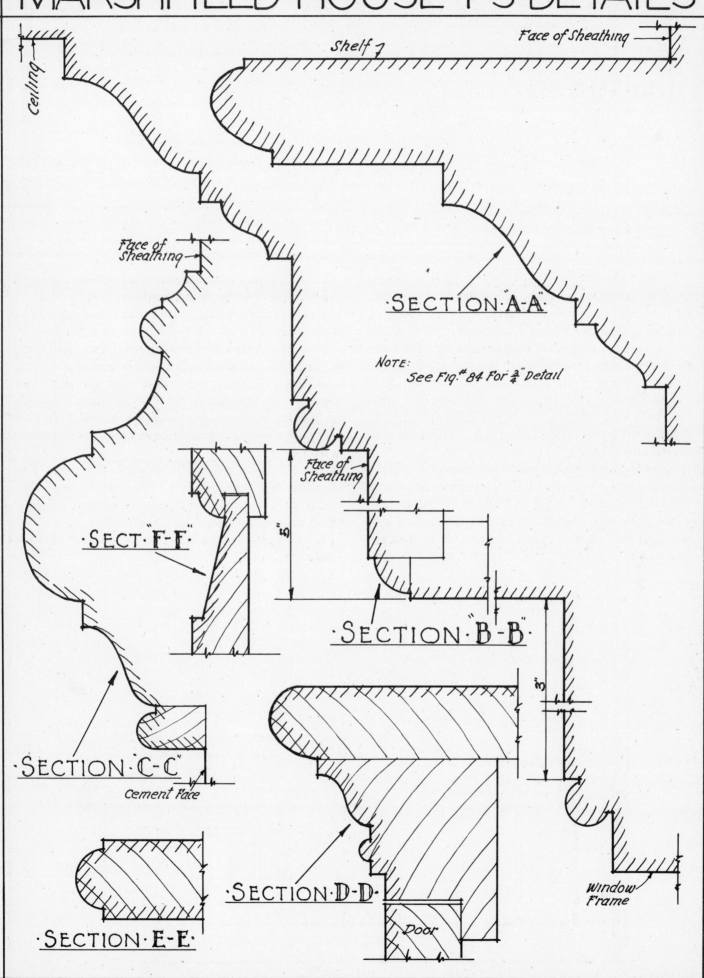

Ceiling

Face of Sheathing

Shelf

·SECTION·"A-A"·

NOTE:
See Fig.# 84 For ¾" Detail

Face of Sheathing

Face of Sheathing

·SECT·"F-F"·

5"

·SECTION·"B-B"·

3"

·SECTION·"C-C"·

Cement Face

·SECTION·"D-D"·

Window Frame

Door

·SECTION·E-E·

FIGURE 85

111

LESSON 32

Brickwork

Every draftsman should be familiar with the common types of bond in brickwork. *Bond* has two meanings, with reference to structure and pattern. *Structural* bond designates the method of overlapping brick to give the wall greater strength. *Pattern* bond has to do with the arrangement of the brick in the face of the wall to give a pleasing appearance. The cost of brickwork varies with the type of bond used since different quantities of brick and varying amounts of labor are involved. Some of the bonds shown in Fig. 86 are described under the following headings:

Common bond (header bond) is the most usual and the cheapest form of brick wall. It consists of a row of "headers" (that is, bricks laid with the short end exposed), then five rows of "stretchers" (bricks laid with the long side exposed), then another row of headers, and so on.

Common bond (Flemish bond) consists of a row of headers and stretchers laid alternately, then five rows of stretchers, then another row of alternate headers and stretchers, and so on. Flemish bond (cross) consists of a row of stretchers in which are included overburned or fire-flashed, dark-colored brick to form the basis for a pattern. The next row consists of stretchers and headers laid alternately, fire-flashed headers making up the pattern, then a row of stretchers, and so on.

English bond consists of alternate courses of stretchers and headers.

Flemish bond consists of courses of headers and stretchers laid alternately.

Gardenwall consists of courses made up of three stretchers, then a header, and so on.

The joints shown in Fig. 86 are the result of different treatments after the bricks are laid.

BRICK BONDS & JOINTS

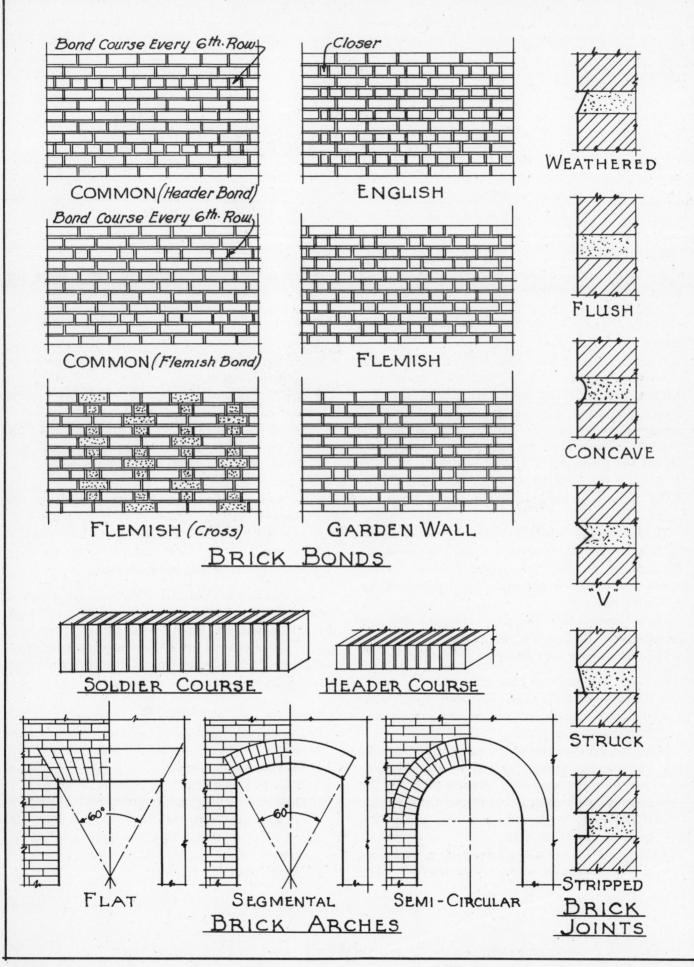

Bond Course Every 6th Row

COMMON (Header Bond)

Bond Course Every 6th Row

COMMON (Flemish Bond)

FLEMISH (Cross)

Closer

ENGLISH

FLEMISH

GARDEN WALL

BRICK BONDS

SOLDIER COURSE

HEADER COURSE

FLAT

SEGMENTAL

SEMI-CIRCULAR

BRICK ARCHES

WEATHERED

FLUSH

CONCAVE

"V"

STRUCK

STRIPPED

BRICK JOINTS

FIGURE 86

113

LESSON 33

Structural Details

The structural details and part plan shown in Fig. 87 are taken from the actual working drawings of an alteration to a school building. The part plan cut off by the broken line shows the framing around a stair well. The framing consists of steel beams and channels carried by a masonry wall and Lally columns, which in turn carry the wood floor joists. The size of the steel is noted on the plan, together with the channels that support the wood joists. Wherever the indication "do" is used, it means that the beams are the same as those noted in a similar position. All beams are made up of standard shapes taken from standard steel handbooks, the size being determined by the span and the load that they must carry. For example, the indication 8" WF-17 means that the beam has an 8" wide flange and weighs 17 lb. per ft.

The section lines with the numbers show where the $\frac{3}{4}$" scale section has been cut, and the arrows indicate the direction in which the section is viewed. These numbers refer to the corresponding numbers on the $\frac{3}{4}$" scale details.

The $\frac{3}{4}$" scale details show the cross-section cuts, and the plan shows the length of the beams.

The sections give the following information:

1. Section 1-1 shows an I beam resting in a pocket in the masonry wall. There is a wall plate (WP2) and angle anchors are used to help support and hold the beam in place.
2. Section 2-2 shows an I beam carrying a terra-cotta tile partition above. The terra-cotta tile partition below the beam does not carry the beam; the beam is supported by the wall and a Lally column. It also shows the floor joists in cross section, the bridging, and the flooring.
3. Section 3-3 shows a beam made up of two channels with channel separators at intervals. The

purpose of this is to allow space between the channels to run heat ducts through. Shelf angles are fastened to the channels to support the floor joists. Note the way in which the floor joists have been cut out.

4. Section 4-4 shows an I beam carrying a terra-cotta tile partition above and a shelf angle attached to support the floor joists.
5. Section 5-5 shows an I beam with a wood partition cap fastened to the underside, to which is nailed the stud partition. A wood stud is set on the top of the beam for nailing the wood-stud partition. Shelf angles are fastened to each side to receive the floor joists.
6. Section 6-6 shows another beam made up of channels and separators to allow heat ducts to pass through. This section shows a Lally column beyond and the wood-stud partitions, together with the shelf angles and floor joists.

Note that all the I beams and channels are the same distance down from the finished floor, $2\frac{3}{4}$", and that the shelf angles are all down 8" from the top of the floor joists. These sections are all thoroughly dimensioned and labeled so that the steel manufacturer can make up his shop drawings and fabricate his steel.

PROBLEM

1. Use 12" x 18" sheet with $\frac{1}{2}$" border line and title box.
2. Plan sheet very carefully.
3. Draw part plan first at $\frac{1}{4}$" scale as shown.
4. Draw the sections in the order given, trying to visualize the cut as you draw. Do not draw any section until you are sure you thoroughly understand it.
5. Use $\frac{3}{4}$" scale for sections.

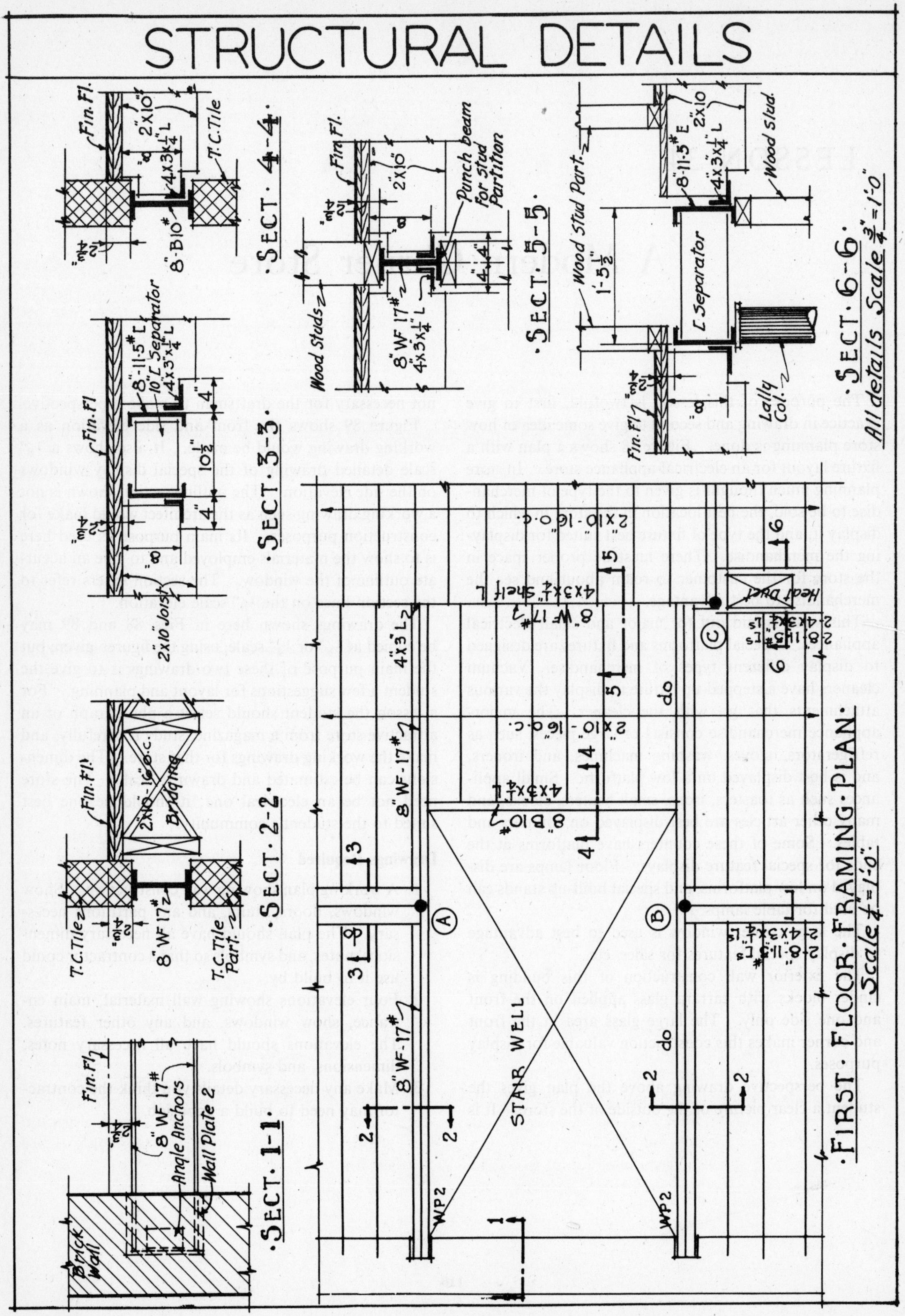

STRUCTURAL DETAILS

FIGURE 87

·SECT·4-4·

Fin. Fl.
2"x10"
T.C.Tile
4"x3"x¼" L
8"·B10#

·SECT·5-5·

Fin. Fl.
2"x10"
Punch beam for Stud Partition
Wood Studs
8" WF 17#
4"x3"x½" L
4"x4"

·SECT·6-6·

All details Scale ¾"=1'-0"

Wood Stud Part.
8"-11.5# E
2"x10"
4"x3"x¼" L
Wood Stud.
L Separator
1'-5½"
8"
Fin. Fl.
Lally Col.

·SECT·3-3·

Fin. Fl.
8"-11.5# L
10" L Separator
4"x3"x½" L
4"
10½"
4"
8"
2"x10 Joist

·SECT·2-2·

Fin. Fl.
2"x10-16"o.c.
Bridging

·SECT·1-1·

Fin. Fl.
8" WF 17#
Angle Anchors
Wall Plate 2
Brick Wall

T.C.Tile
8" WF 17#
T.C. Tile Part.

·FIRST·FLOOR·FRAMING·PLAN·

Scale ¼"=1'-0"

2"x10-16"o.c.
4"x3"x½" Shelf L
8" WF 17#
4"x3" L's
8" WF 17#
Heat Duct
2-4"x3"x½" L's
8"-11.5# L's
do
C
2"x10-16"o.c.
4"x3"x½" L
8"-B10#
4"x3"x½" L's
2-8"-11.5# L's
A
B
STAIR WELL
WP 2
WP 2
do
2
2
2
2
3
1
4
5
5
6
6

LESSON 34

A Modern Corner Store

The purpose of this lesson is twofold, first to give practice in drawing and second to give some idea of how store planning is done. Figure 88 shows a plan with a fixture layout for an electrical-appliance store. In store planning much thought is given to the type of merchandise to be sold, the best location in the store in which to display it, and the type of fixture best suited for displaying the merchandise. There must be proper space in the store for the customer to roam about and see the merchandise to best advantage.

This store is laid out for major and small electrical appliances. Special platforms and fixtures are designed to display different types of merchandise. Vacuum cleaners have a stepped-up fixture to display the various attachments that go with the cleaner. The major-appliance merchandise consists of large pieces, such as refrigerators, stoves, washing machines, and ironers, and is best displayed on a low platform. Small appliances such as toasters, irons, small heaters, clocks, and many other articles are best displayed on counters and tables. Some of these counters have platforms at the ends for special feature displays. Floor lamps are displayed on low platforms, and special built-up stands can be used for table lamps.

The large corner window is used to best advantage to display special features for sales, etc.

The exterior wall construction of this building is cinder blocks with carrara glass applied on the front and one side only. The large glass area in the front and corner makes this construction valuable for display purposes.

The perspective drawing above the plan gives the student a clear picture of the outside of the store. It is not necessary for the draftsman to make a perspective.

Figure 89 shows the front and side elevation as a working drawing would be made. It also shows a $\frac{1}{8}''$ scale detailed drawing of the special display windows on the side elevation. The outline section shown is not a working drawing such as the architect would make for construction purposes. Its main purpose as used here is to show the materials employed and to give an accurate outline of the window. The section letters refer to the section lines on the $\frac{1}{8}''$ scale elevation.

The drawings shown here in Figs. 88 and 89 may be copied at $\frac{1}{8}''$ or $\frac{1}{4}''$ scale, using the figures given, but the main purpose of these two drawings is to give the student a few suggestions for layout and planning. For a lesson the student should select a photograph of an attractive store from a magazine, study it carefully, and make the working drawings for that store. The dimensions can be estimated and drawn to scale. The store need not be an electrical one; it should be one best suited to the student's community.

Drawings Required

1. A working plan showing wall construction. Show windows, doors, stairs, and any partitions necessary. The plan should have all necessary dimensions, notes, and symbols so that a contractor could use it to build by.
2. Four elevations showing wall material, main entrance, show windows, and any other features. The elevations should have all necessary notes, dimensions, and symbols.
3. Make any necessary details you think the contractor may need to build a good job.

MODERN CORNER STORE

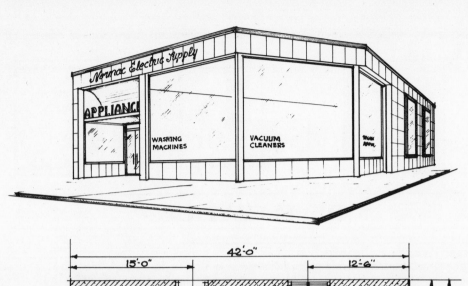

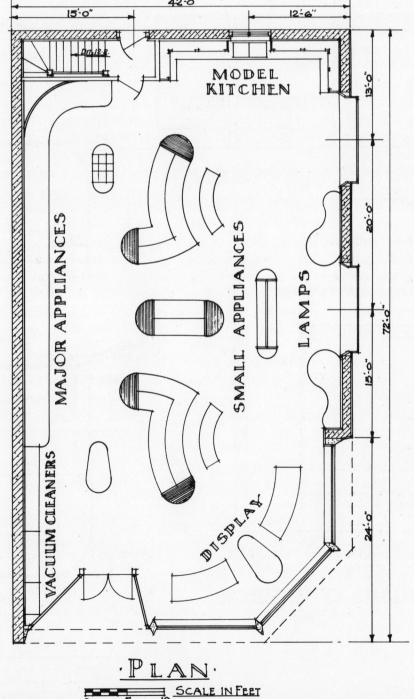

NOTE:
See Fig. #89 For
Elevations and
Details.

42'-0"

15'-0"

12'-6"

MODEL
KITCHEN

13'-0"

20'-0"

72'-0"

15'-0"

24'-0"

MAJOR APPLIANCES

SMALL APPLIANCES

LAMPS

VACUUM CLEANERS

DISPLAY

·PLAN·

SCALE IN FEET

0   5   10

FIGURE 88

117

MODERN CORNER STORE

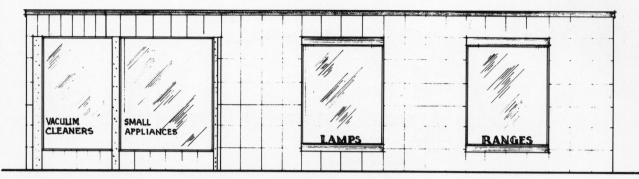

SIDE · ELEVATION ·

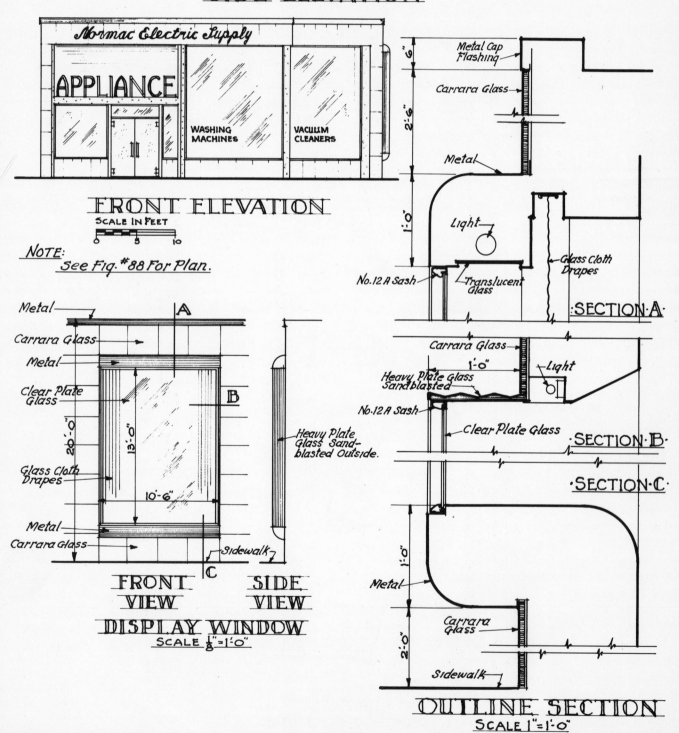

Normac Electric Supply

APPLIANCE

WASHING MACHINES

VACUUM CLEANERS

FRONT ELEVATION

SCALE IN FEET

0   5   10

NOTE:
See Fig. #88 For Plan.

Metal Cap Flashing

Carrara Glass

2'-6"

Metal

1'-0"

Light

No.12 A Sash

Translucent Glass

Glass Cloth Drapes

·SECTION·A·

Carrara Glass

Heavy Plate Glass Sandblasted

1'-0"

Light

No.12 A Sash

Clear Plate Glass

·SECTION·B·

·SECTION·C·

Metal

Carrara Glass

Metal

Clear Plate Glass

20'-0"

13'-0"

Glass Cloth Drapes

10'-6"

Metal

Carrara Glass

Heavy Plate Glass Sandblasted Outside.

Sidewalk

A

B

C

FRONT VIEW   SIDE VIEW

DISPLAY WINDOW

SCALE ⅛"=1'-0"

Metal

1'-0"

Carrara Glass

2'-0"

Sidewalk

OUTLINE SECTION

SCALE 1"=1'-0"

FIGURE 89

118

LESSON 35

Department-store Fixtures

Figures 90 to 92 show how the working drawings are made for the construction of department-store fixtures. In some cases the designer would make a few more full-size details of the important parts of the case. When the mill receives this working drawing, it is turned over to the draftsman who does the layout work for the shop. He lays out most of his work at full size, showing all the necessary construction and blocking.

In drawing store fixtures, it is necessary to show the front, top, and end views, together with a section showing the construction. An isometric pictorial drawing is always a great help, for it gives a clear picture of the finished product. If there are any moldings or intricate parts of the fixture that cannot be shown at small scale, they should be drawn at full size. All dimensions and notes should be put in clearly and precisely in order to make the work in the shop as easy as possible. If the detail is complete in all respects, there will be less questioning and delay in the construction. Also, a more accurate estimated cost can be obtained from a complete drawing.

NOTES ABOUT FIXTURES

Duplex Yard-goods Display Case (see Fig. 90)

This fixture is used for the display of yard goods, which come in rolls known as *bolts*. The bolts are placed in the case on end, giving a full view of the material and allowing the customer to inspect it without the aid of a salesperson. There is space below for storage of extra stock. The advantage of this fixture over table tops is that it carries more stock, displays the goods to better advantage, and allows the customer to look the stock over, thus saving the time of the salesperson.

Hosiery Display Case (see Fig. 91)

This case is used for the display of men's hosiery according to size and price. The sign mold running through the middle is used for small cards designating the size and price of the hosiery. There is ample space below for stock. This type of fixture can be used for a system known as *simplified selling*, according to which the goods are displayed according to size and the customer serves himself in selecting the article and gives it to a salesperson, who completes the sale.

Typical Showcase (see Fig. 92)

Many types of showcases are used in department stores. The design is determined by the kind of merchandise to be sold. The showcase shown here is a typical case that could be used for almost any kind of merchandise. The length varies to fit the many conditions. The rear view shows drawers and shelves for stock. This stock space can be revised to meet conditions. For modern store-fixture design, the modular system of making interchangeable units of stock sizes is much used. With this system islands of almost any length and in various combinations can be made up.

PROBLEM

Procedure for Drawing Store Fixtures

1. Use 12″ x 18″ sheet with ½″ border and title.
2. Lay out all work very lightly at first.
3. Draw front, top, and side view by third-angle projection (see Fig. 40). Use same scale as shown.
4. It is a good idea to work up the construction section as you proceed with the front, top, and end views. There are many points that the section brings out that will not show in the other drawings.
5. After drawings are blocked out completely, put on all dimensions, notes, and material symbols.
6. Draw complete isometric view of fixture (see Fig. 39 for isometric drawing).

DEPARTMENT-STORE FIXTURE

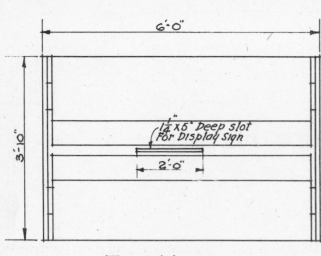

6'-0"

3'-10"

1¼"x5" Deep slot
For Display sign

2'-0"

· TOP VIEW ·

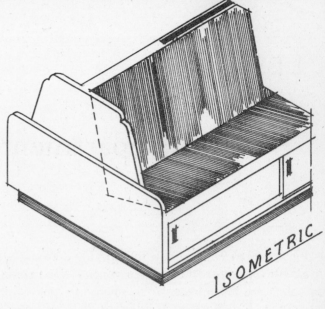

· ISOMETRIC ·

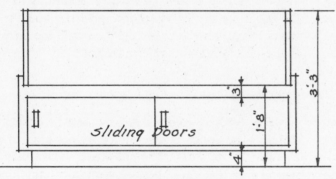

Sliding Doors

3"

1'-8"

4"

3'-3"

· FRONT VIEW ·

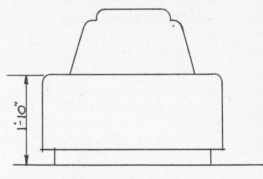

1'-10"

· END VIEW ·

Scale ½"=1'-0"

· DUPLEX YARD GOODS DISPLAY CASE ·

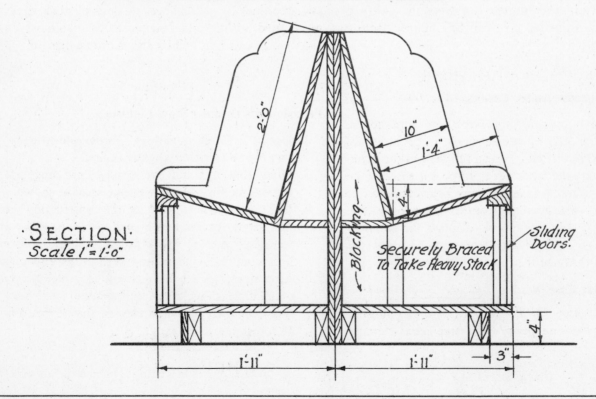

· SECTION ·
Scale 1"=1'-0"

2'-0"

10"

1'-4"

4"

Blocking

Securely Braced
To Take Heavy Stock

Sliding
Doors.

1'-11"

1'-11"

3"

4"

FIGURE 90

120

DEPARTMENT-STORE FIXTURE

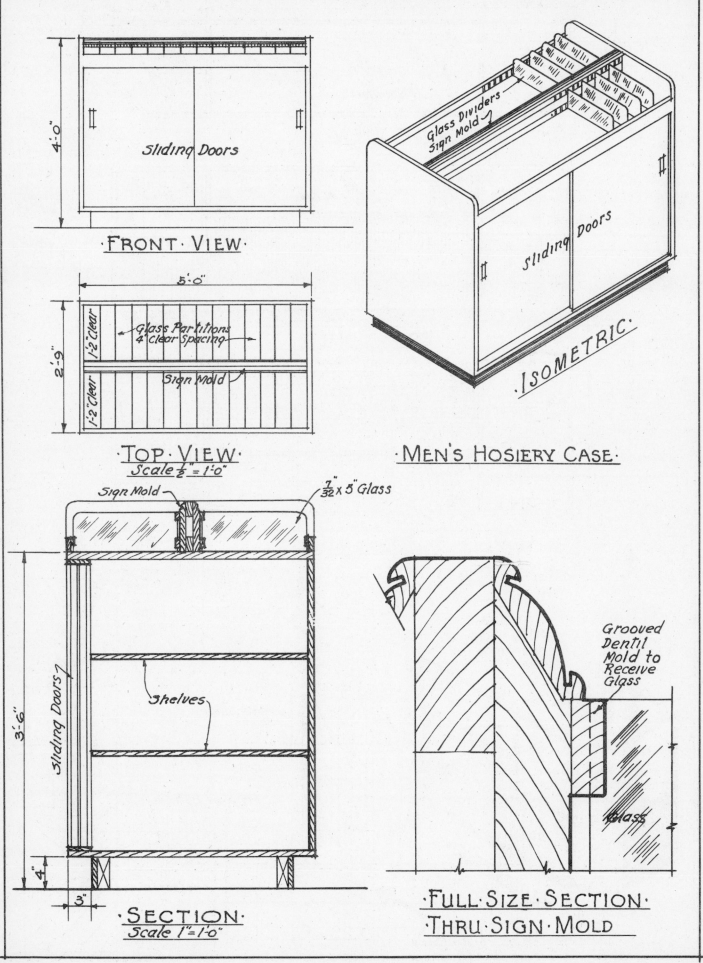

·FRONT·VIEW·

4'-0"

Sliding Doors

·TOP·VIEW·
Scale ½"=1'-0"

5'-0"

2'-9"

1'-2" Clear

1'-2" Clear

Glass Partitions
4" Clear Spacing

Sign Mold

·ISOMETRIC·

Glass Dividers
Sign Mold

Sliding Doors

·MEN'S HOSIERY CASE·

Sign Mold

$\frac{7}{32}$" x 5" Glass

Sliding Doors

Shelves

3'-6"

4"

3"

·SECTION·
Scale 1"=1'-0"

Grooved
Dentil
Mold to
Receive
Glass

Glass

·FULL·SIZE·SECTION·
THRU·SIGN·MOLD

FIGURE 91

121

DEPARTMENT-STORE FIXTURE

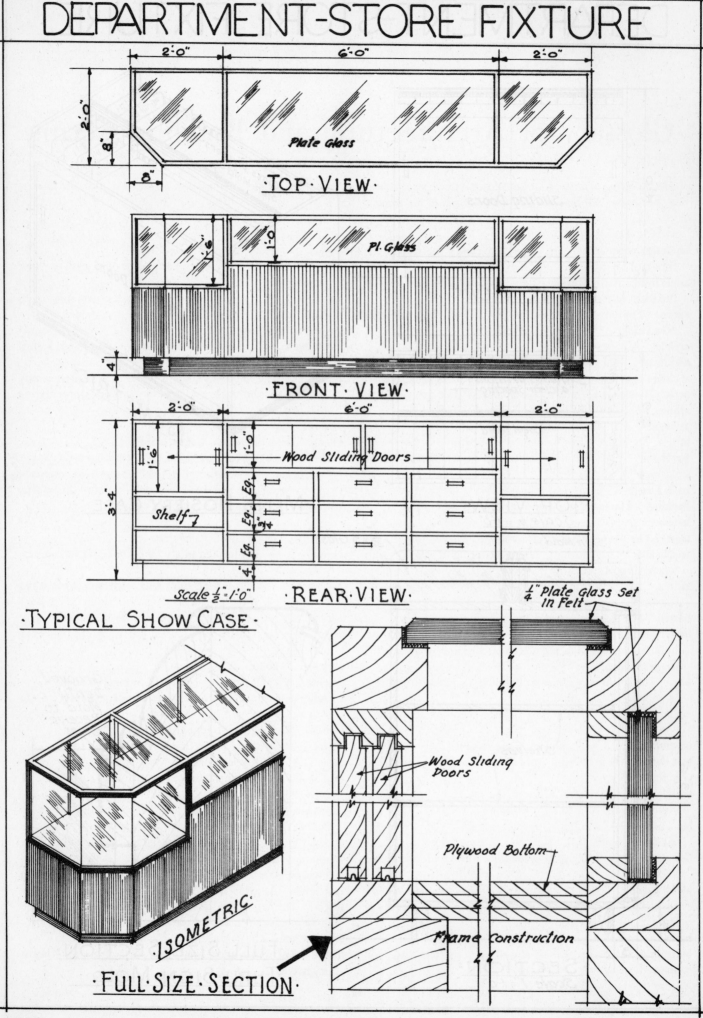

2'-0" 6'-0" 2'-0"

2'-0"

8"

8"

Plate Glass

· TOP · VIEW ·

1'-6"

1'-0"

Pl. Glass

4"

· FRONT · VIEW ·

2'-0" 6'-0" 2'-0"

1'-6"

1'-0"

Wood Sliding Doors

Eq.

Eq.

Eq.

Eq.

3"

4"

4"

3'-4"

Shelf

Scale ½"=1'-0"   · REAR · VIEW ·

· TYPICAL SHOW CASE ·

¼" Plate Glass Set in Felt

Wood Sliding Doors

Plywood Bottom

Frame Construction

· ISOMETRIC ·

· FULL · SIZE · SECTION ·

FIGURE 92

122

Glossary of Architectural and Building Terms

The following definitions and explanations of architectural and building terms in common use is intended to assist apprentices and others not familiar with the language of the trade.

abutment of an arch. The mass of masonry that resists the thrust of an arch.

angle iron. A structural iron shape whose cross section is in the form of a letter L.

apron. The finish board placed immediately below a window stool.

arcade. A series of arches.

architrave. The molded finish around an opening, also called the *trim*. The lower division of an entablature.

arris. The edge formed by the intersection of two surfaces.

ashlar. The outside cut-stone facing of a wall.

astragal. A small molding of circular section.

attic. The space immediately under the roof of a house.

backband. The outside member of a window or door casing.

back hearth. The part of a hearth inside the fireplace.

backing. The inner portion of a wall.

balcony. A platform projecting from the wall of a building.

base. The lower member of a column or a building.

baseboard. The finishing board covering a plaster wall where it meets the floor.

batten. A strip of board for use in fastening other boards together.

batter. The slope of a wall face that is not plumb.

batter boards. Boards set up at the corners of a proposed building from which are stretched the lines marking off the walls, etc.

bay. The space between two columns; also a small projecting portion of a building.

beam. A large horizontal structural member supporting floors, etc.

bearing wall. A wall carrying more than its own weight.

belt course. A projection from the wall carried around the building.

bond. The connections between the bricks or stones of a masonry wall, formed by overlapping the pieces.

box frame. A window frame containing boxes for the window weights.

bridging. Cross bracing between floor joists to add stiffness to the floors.

building line. The line of the outside face of a building wall; also, the line on a lot beyond which the law forbids a building to be erected.

building paper. A heavy waterproof paper.

buttress. The projection of a wall to resist the thrust of an arch.

butts. Hinges for doors or windows.

camber. The convex curve of the edge of a joist or other member.

carriage. The framing timber that is the direct support of stair steps.

casement. A hinged window.

catch basin. A receptacle into which water from a roof areaway, etc., drains.

centering. The false work upon which are built masonry arches, concrete slabs, etc. In concrete work the centering is also known as the *forms*.

channel. A structural steel shape.

client. The employer of the architect.

coffer. A deeply recessed panel.

collar beam. A horizontal timber tying two opposite rafters together at a more or less center point of the rafters.

colonnade. A continuous series of columns.

coped joint. A portion of one member cut out to receive the molded part of another member.

corbel. A bracket formed in a wall by building out successive courses of masonry.

corner bead. A metal bead built into corners to prevent the breaking off of the plaster.

cornice. The part of a roof that projects beyond the wall.

court. An open space surrounded partly or entirely by a building.

cresting. The top of a wall.

cupola. A small structure on top of a dome or roof.

curtain wall. A thin wall supported independently of the wall below.

dentils. Rectangular supporting blocks.

dormer. A structure projecting from a sloping roof.

drain. A means of carrying off waste water.

drip mold. A molding designed to protect the bottom of doors and windows from leakage.

elevations. Drawings of the walls of a building made as though the observer were looking straight at the wall.

entablature. The superstructure lying horizontally upon columns; divided into architrave, frieze, cornice.

escutcheon plate. The protective metal plate at a keyhole.

face brick. A special brick used for facing a wall.

fascia. The flat vertical member of the cornice; one of the three bands that make up the architrave.

fenestration. The arrangement of windows in a wall.

flange. The upper and lower cross parts of a steel I beam or channel.

flashing. The sheet-metal work that prevents leakage over windows, doors, etc., around chimneys, and at other roof details.

floor plan. The horizontal section through a building showing the size and location of rooms, also doors, windows, etc., in the walls.

flue. A passage in the chimney to convey smoke to the outer air.

footing. The spread portion at the bottom of a basement wall or column to prevent settlement.

fresco. The painting on fresh plaster before it has dried.

furring. The leveling up or building out of a part of a wall or ceiling by wood strips, etc.

gable. The triangular portion of an end wall formed by the sloping roof.

gable roof. A roof sloping up from two walls.

gambrel roof. A roof having two different slopes.

gargoyle. An ornamental water spout that throws the roof water clear of the walls below.

girder. A large horizontal structural member, usually heavier than a beam and used to support the ends of joists and beams or to carry walls over openings.

girt. The heavy horizontal timber carrying the second-floor joists in a braced frame building.

grade. The level of the ground around a building.

grille. A protective metal screen.

ground. Strips of wood, the thickness of the plaster of a wall, secured to the framing. They aid the plasterer and afterward serve as nailing strips for securing the finish.

grout. A thin mortar for filling up spaces to which access is difficult or to which the heavier mortar would not penetrate.

gutter. A trough or depression for carrying off water.

halving. A method of splicing the ends of two timbers.

hatching. The shading of an imaginary cut surface by a series of parallel lines.

headroom. The vertical clearance on a stairway or in a room.

hearth. The masonry portion of a floor in front of a fireplace.

heel. The end of a rafter that rests on the wall plate.

hip roof. A roof sloping up from all walls of the building.

hood. The small roof over a doorway.

house drain. The piping that carries off the discharge from all soil and waste lines.

house sewer. The drainage pipe connecting with the house drain about 10′ outside the building.

housing. The part cut out of one member so as to receive another.

impost. The top member of a wall, pier, etc., from which springs an arch.

incise. To cut into, as letters incised or carved into stone.

jamb. The inside vertical face of a door or window frame.

joist. The framing timbers that are the direct support of a floor.

keystone. The center top stone of an arch.

Lally column. A steel pipe filled with concrete; used as a supporting member for carrying heavy loads.

lantern. The small structure projecting above a dome or roof for light or ventilation.

lean-to. A small building against the side of another and having a roof sloping away from the larger structure.

lintel. The horizontal structural member supporting the wall over an opening.

lobby. An entrance hall or waiting room.

loggia. A hall within a building but open on one side.

lookout. A short timber for supporting a projecting cornice.

louver. A ventilating window covered by sloping slats to exclude rain.

mansard roof. A hipped roof having two slopes similar to the gambrel roof.

mantel. The shelf over a fireplace.

meeting rail. The horizontal center rails of a sash.

mezzanine. A low secondary story contained in a high story.

millwork. Finished woodwork, machined and partly assembled at the mill.

miter. The beveled surface cut on the ends of molding.

modillion. An ornamental bracket supporting a cornice.

mullion. The large vertical division of a window opening.

muntins. The small members that divide the glass in a sash.

narthex. A hall or lobby at the entrance of a church.

nave. The main or central portion of a church auditorium.

newel. The post where the handrail of a stair starts or changes direction.

niche. A recess in a wall.

ogee. A reverse-curve molding.

oriel window. A projecting upper story window; a small bay.

orientation. The direction of facing of a building.

panel. A piece of wood framed about by other pieces.

parapet. The part of a wall projecting above the roof.

parting strip. The strip in a double-hung window frame that keeps the upper and lower sash apart.

party wall. A division wall common to two adjacent pieces of property.

pier. A rectangle masonry support either built into a wall or free standing.

pilaster. An attached pier, high in proportion to its width.

piling. Wood or concrete posts driven down into earth to provide safe footing for heavy loads.

pitch of roof. A term applied to the amount of slope.

plan. See floor plan.

plancher or **plancier.** The soffit of a cornice.

plate. The top horizontal timber of a wall; the attic joist, roof rafters, etc., rest on and are secured to the plate.

plinth. The block that forms the bottom member of a column base; also used as a base for the heavy architrave of a door or window.

plumb. Vertical; parallel to a plumb line.

porch. A covered shelter on the outside of a building.

priming. The first coat of paint or varnish, mixed and applied so as to fill the pores of the surface preparatory to receiving the subsequent coats.

proscenium. The front part of a theater stage including the arch over the stage.

purlins. Structural members spanning from truss to truss and supporting the rafters of a roof.

quoins. Large cut stones at the corners of a masonry wall.

rail. The horizontal top member of a balustrade; also, the horizontal members of windows and doors.

rabbet. A recess cut in a doorframe to receive the door.

relieving arch. A masonry arch built over an opening to support the backing of a wall when the wall face is carried by a lintel.

return. A molding turned back into the wall on which it is located.

ridge. The top edge of the roof where two slopes meet.

rostrum. An elevated speaker's platform.

rotunda. The circular space under a dome.

rubble. Roughly broken quarrystone.

saddle. A small double-sloping roof to carry the water away from the back of chimneys.

scale. An instrument used for measuring. Scale in design is the feeling of size that is produced by the use of doors, windows, etc.

scratch coat. The first coat of plaster, which is scratched or scored to form a good bond for the second coat.

screed. Gauge for the thickness of plaster on a wall.

scribe. To mark or fit one edge of a board, etc., to an irregular surface.

sheathing. The rough boarding on the outside of a wall or roof over which is laid the finished siding or the shingles.

shoring. Timbers for temporary support, braced against a wall where the wall below is to be removed.

show rafter. A short rafter extending below the cornice.

sill. The bottom timber laid on a firm foundation to carry and secure the superstructure.

smoke chamber. The part of a flue directly above the fireplace damper.

soffit. The under surface of a cornice, beam, etc.

soil stack. The pipe that runs into a house drain from the soil pipe.

span. The distance between beams, joists, etc.

specifications. The written or printed description of materials, workmanship, etc., that accompany the working drawings of a building.

standing finish. The finish wood secured to the walls.

stile. The vertical members of a built-up part such as a door.

stool. The wood shelf across the bottom and inside of a window.

string. The supporting timber at the end of stair steps.

stucco. Cement plaster for outside work.

terrace. A raised bank of earth.

terra cotta. A burned clay of fine quality.

thimble. The horizontal pipe running through a chimney wall into the flue.

threshold. The stone, wood, or metal piece directly under a door.

transom. A small window over a door.

tread. The horizontal board of a step.

trellis. An ornamental wooden lattice.

trim. The finishing frame around an opening.

trimmer arch. The supporting arch for a fireplace hearth.

truss. A built-up framework for supporting loads over large spans.

underpinning. The new part of a wall or pier, built under an existing part.

valley. The intersection of two roof slopes.

valley rafter. The rafter extending along under a valley.

veneer. A thin covering of valuable material over a less expensive body.

vent pipes. Small ventilating pipes extending from each fixture of a plumbing system to the vent stack.

verge boards. The boards running down the slope of a roof from the top of the gable; also called *rake boards*.

vestibule. A small entrance room.

voussoir. One of the sections or blocks of an arch.

wainscot. An ornamental or protective covering of walls.

water table. The projecting sloping member around a building near the ground to throw rain water away from the wall.

yoke. The horizontal top member of a window frame.

Index